WELDING

WELDING

Len Gourd

TEACH YOURSELF BOOKS

Hodder and Stoughton

First published 1989

British Library Cataloguing in Publication Data
Gourd, L. M.
Welding.
1. Welding
I. Title
671.5'2

ISBN 0 340 49316 X

Printed in Great Britain for
Hodder and Stoughton Educational,
a division of Hodder and Stoughton Ltd,
Mill Road, Dunton Green, Sevenoaks, Kent,
by Richard Clay Ltd, Bungay, Suffolk.
Photoset by Rowland Phototypesetting Ltd,
Bury St Edmunds, Suffolk.

Contents

Part Two Welding Practices

Before You Start

If you asked someone 'What do you think about welding?' the response would almost certainly be a puzzled expression. If pushed, the majority of people would probably answer 'Not a lot!'. In a way, this is a tribute to the effectiveness of welding as a method of joining components together. It's so good under most circumstances that we do not give it a second thought even if we notice it!

But you have bought this book so obviously you have some special reason for wanting to know about welding. You might be a practising welder. Perhaps you come across it in your daily work. Maybe you have bought or are thinking of buying one of the many DIY kits on sale in the magazines. Possibly you are just curious. Whatever your interest, the aim of this book is to give you an insight into both the technology and the practical aspects of one of the most fascinating craft skills still in industrial use.

The book is in two parts. The first paints the scene and looks at the background to welding. Chapters 1 to 5 develop the theme of technology and should be read as a continuing sequence. Inevitably in such a short space the subject cannot be treated in great depth. Nor can it be exhaustive – after a lifetime in welding, the author is still learning new aspects of the subject. A number of explanations must of necessity be brief but hopefully will lead you on to further reading and discovery. Make a point of looking around at your place of work or when you are walking past steel structures such as bridges and see if you can identify any welded joints. Try to decide how they were made and think of any problems the welder may have been faced with. When you have finished the book you can explore different aspects of welding by reading some of the books listed in the Appendix.

Part 1 starts by reviewing the scope of welding in modern practice and goes on to arc welding when we will look at how different types of welds are made. There is a diversity of techniques available and it is important to recognise their uses and limitations if we are to get the best results. We'll also take on board the problem of deciding what we mean by a good weld and think about how different metals react to welding.

In the second part of the book we will be concentrating on the practical aspects together with some thoughts on how to learn to weld. One very important topic will be safety. You are probably familiar with the bright light given off by the arc which can damage your eyes, but there are other less obvious hazards like fume and electric shock which you need to know about if you are going to use welding.

If you are a welder by trade, the book covers the job knowledge which is essential for an understanding of the craft. In many internationally used standards welders are being asked to demonstrate not just their practical skill but also that they understand the basic principles of the technology. I hope you will find this book of value in meeting these requirements. You should be able to find the answer to many job knowledge test questions in the following pages.

Finally, if you are a DIY enthusiast, the book will help you decide which process offers the most advantages for the type of work you have in mind. It will also highlight some of the important aspects which need to be considered before purchasing a welding set.

PART ONE
Welding Principles

1

The Role of Welding

Welding has been one of the most significant manufacturing processes during the last half century. Many of the things we take for granted would not be possible or would be too costly were it not for the widespread use of welding in industry. The development of commodities as widely different as washing machines and jet engines would have been severely hampered if the appropriate welding technique had not been available to the designer.

We can get a better idea of what this means by looking at some typical products and trying to identify the role of welding in their manufacture.

Welding in modern industry

Let's start with the modern car. The body shell is made by joining together a number of panels or sections pressed from sheet steel. Individually the parts are not very strong. They are flexible and can be easily twisted out of shape. Joined together, however, they form a rigid body capable of carrying passengers without collapsing. For this to happen the joints between the panels must be strong.

At the same time, we want to produce the car bodies quickly so they must be easily made. We could use rivets as in an aircraft. A rivetted joint might give the strength we need but the production would be slow and the car would be very expensive. Welding also gives good strength but most importantly works fast and is relatively cheap.

Take a look around a car, particularly underneath. You should be able to recognise examples of the joints shown in Fig. 1.1.

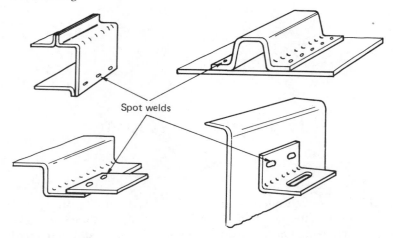

Fig. 1.1   Typical resistance welded joints in a car

Resistance welding

Sketch the cross-sections of the joints on a piece of paper and you will see that in all of them the sheets are bent or flanged at the joint to bring two surfaces into contact.

This is a lap joint and it is usually made with spot welds. We can recognise the position of a spot weld by the slight depression on the surface. Suppose we cut a section through a spot weld (Fig. 1.2a). We will see that there is a length of solid metal between the two sheets at the interface in line with the surface depressions. This is the weld which provides the link between the sheets and gives strength to the joint.

We can learn a lot more about the weld by attacking the surface of the section with acid. This is known as etching and it reveals the structure of the metal (Fig. 1.2b). Viewed through a magnifying lens or a microscope, each metal has a characteristic structure. In a sense we are looking at the fingerprint of the joint.

An etched section through a joint is called a **macrosection** and it can show us what welding has done to the metal. You will find a number of macrosections in this book.

For a start, Fig. 1.2b is a macrosection of a spot weld which has been magnified five times. There is an area around the interface which is darker than the sheet material. If you look closely you can see that in this area there is a pattern of lines radiating out from the interface. This is the crystal structure of a metal which has been molten and allowed to solidify and is different from the sheet which at this magnification looks featureless. The macrosection tells us that the weld was made by fusing (melting) the steel at the interface so that the liquid metal from both sheets mixed. When the molten slug cooled it solidified as one piece which was bonded (joined) to both sheets. The process used for this operation is called resistance welding because the heat needed to melt the steel is generated by passing an electric current through the interface. The interface offers a resistance to the flow of the current and heat is generated in the same way as in a domestic electric fire. But, in the case of resistance welding, the current is significantly higher. A 2 kilowatt (kW) electric fire takes a current of about 8 amperes (A) whereas a

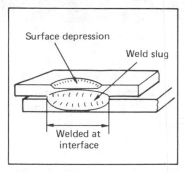

Fig. 1.2(a) Cross-section of a spot weld in a steel sheet

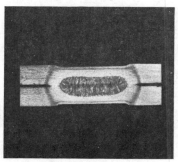

Fig. 1.2(b) A macrosection

Fig. 1.3   Resistance welding in use in car manufacture

resistance weld needs something of the order of 2000A. At this current level the weld is made in a few tenths of a second.

Resistance welding is ideally suited to rapid production of welded joints. It can be used manually by operators or it can be incorporated into a robot line. We will take a closer look at resistance welding in Chapter 11.

Fusion welding

It is not always possible or desirable to use a resistance welded lap joint. The metal may be difficult to bend or it may be too thick for resistance welding. In these cases, we would use fusion welding.

The principles of fusion welding are well illustrated by a welded T-joint. The bridge between the two plates which make up the T is in the form of a gusset or fillet along the length of the joint line. The cross-section (Fig. 1.4) shows that the fillet has been fused into the surfaces of the sheet. For this type of weld we need to supply heat from an external source.

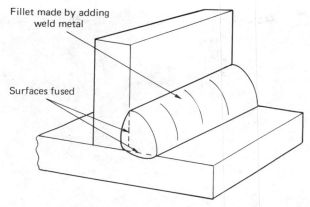

Fillet made by adding weld metal

Surfaces fused

Fig. 1.4 Fusion welded T-joint

Oxy-acetylene welding

If you go along to your local repair garage, you will probably see the mechanic using oxy-acetylene welding. This process uses a flame to melt both the surfaces of the joint and the wire which is added to make the fillet. We cannot use just any flame; the gas supplied for your cooker is unsuitable because it burns at too low a temperature. The flame must be very hot otherwise the heat flows away from the joint before the surfaces have been raised to the melting temperature of the metal. A mixture of acetylene and oxygen burns with a flame temperature of about 3100°C which is just hot enough to fuse the metal (Fig. 1.5).

Oxy-acetylene welding is no longer used to any great extent in the car production industry because it is slow and requires highly skilled operators.

Arc welding

The electric arc is a much more effective device for welding. An arc is formed when electricity flows across a gap between two conductors. In the case of welding, the conductors are the workpiece, on the one hand, and a metal wire called an electrode. The current for welding is supplied by a power supply unit, commonly known as a **power source**, which plugs into the mains supply and reduces the voltage to that needed for the arc. The power source also isolates

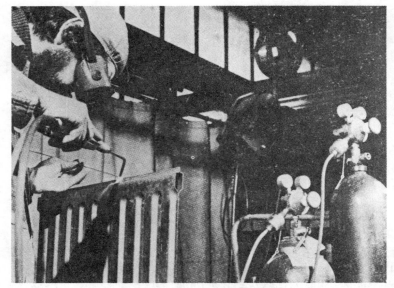

Fig. 1.5   Oxy-acetylene welding radiator panels

the welder from the mains so that the risk of electrocution is minimized.

The current flows from the power source, along the electrode, across the arc gap, and returns via the workpiece (Fig. 1.6a).

The first thing we notice about the arc is that it emits a bright light which contains ultraviolet rays. These can produce an effect similar to sunburn and the arc can only be viewed through a special filter designed to eliminate the ultraviolet light and reduce the level of brightness. The power of the arc is not located in the gap, where the light comes from, but at the surface of the workpiece and the tip of the electrode: this gives us heat where we want it. At the surface of the work we get the fusion which is essential for bonding and the heat at the tip of the electrode melts the filler metal needed to make the fillet (Fig. 1.6).

Fig. 1.6b shows a MIG welding gun which is widely used for joining steel and aluminium. The name is an abbreviation of metal inert gas welding and we will be learning more about this process in the next chapter together with other important arc welding systems.

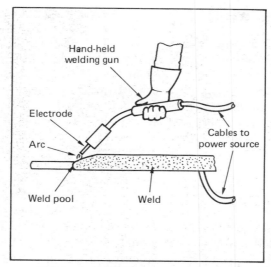

Fig. 1.6(a) MIG welding sheet steel

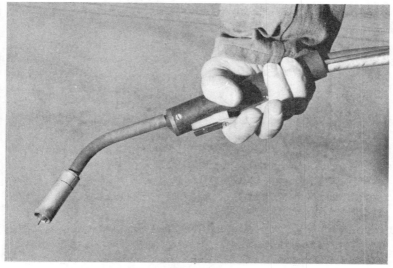

Fig. 1.6(b) MIG welding

Welding heavy structures

Cars are made from thin sheets of steel. Usually the thickness is somewhere between 0.8 mm and 1.6 mm. If you are familiar with sheet metal work, you might recognise these sizes as 22swg (Standard Wire Gauge) and 16swg. By way of contrast we can look at structures made from steel plate. Ships, bridges and power station boilers are fabricated from plates and sections which have thicknesses ranging from 6 to 75 mm (i.e. ¼ in to 3 in). Before World War Two the standard method of jointing would have been rivetting. Lap joints were used for butts and T-joints were flanged. This doubled the thickness at the joint line and caused a considerable increase in weight. Welding not only gives a better profile and leads to a reduction in overall weight, it also allows the structure to work under greater stress. It is difficult to imagine a super-tanker with rivetted joints; the joints would probably 'give' under load and the whole ship would be unstable. Rivetted joints are difficult to

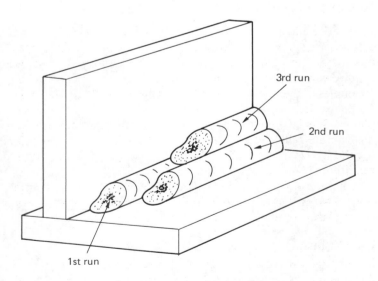

Fig. 1.7   Building up the size of a fillet weld

make leaktight whereas welding produces a continuous joint so that welded boilers and chemical plant can operate at much higher pressures, making their operation far more efficient.

T-joints in plate can be arc welded in much the same way as with sheet. The arc melts the surfaces of the plates and electrode metal is added to form the fillet. The welder starts at one end of the joint and moves the arc at a steady speed to keep the size of the fillet uniform. This technique produces a single weld run – sometimes called a single pass weld. There is a limitation on the size of the weld we can make by just moving along the joint once. If we try to make the weld run too large, the molten weld metal runs out of the joint and we end up with an unsatisfactory misshapen deposit. The answer is to use a number of smaller runs to build up the weld to the desired size (Fig. 1.7).

Butt joints are treated in a similar way. The edges are bevelled so that when they are put together they form a groove. The weld is made by filling the groove with a number of passes which are fused into the plate and to each other.

Newer processes

Resistance and arc welding have become the mainstay of manufacturing industry especially where steel is used. But the advent of new materials, both metal and plastics, has posed problems which require newer joining techniques to be developed for their solution. Examples of these new demands are the increased use of aluminium for lightweight structures and stainless steel for chemical processing plants. Special metals such as Nimonic and titanium are widely incorporated into jet engines. When plastic pipes were developed for the transmission of gas and water, a whole new set of joining requirements were introduced.

A number of processes have been developed for these applications. Two groups stand out and are worth looking at: beam welding – using lasers or electron beams – and pressure welding.

Laser welding

Lasers have become familiar in recent years thanks to TV documentaries and science fiction films. They are devices which produce a highly concentrated beam of light focused onto a spot on the surface of a material. The lasers used for scenic lighting effects and for surgical operations on the eye are relatively low powered. However, high powered lasers with energy outputs of the order of 10 to 25 kW are available for industrial use. We can get some idea of the magnitude of this power if we remember that a light bulb is rated at 100 watts (W) i.e. one tenth of a kilowatt (0.1kW). With the industrial laser, the power of 100 to 250 light bulbs is used to produce a concentrated spot of light with a diameter of about 2 mm. The effect on a piece of metal is rapidly to raise the temperature of the surface under the beam until the metal vaporises. A crater or depression is formed. The metal at the bottom of the crater is vaporized and the process continues until a hole has been drilled

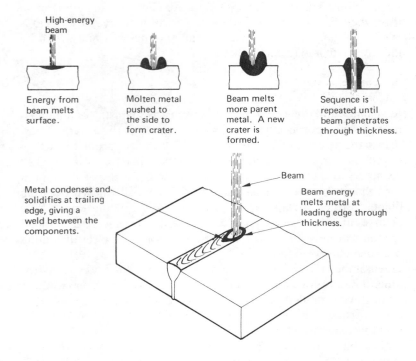

High-energy beam

Energy from beam melts surface.

Molten metal pushed to the side to form crater.

Beam melts more parent metal. A new crater is formed.

Sequence is repeated until beam penetrates through thickness.

Metal condenses and solidifies at trailing edge, giving a weld between the components.

Beam

Beam energy melts metal at leading edge through thickness.

Fig. 1.8   Principles of keyholing

through the thickness of the metal. The diameter of the hole is only slightly larger than the diameter of the beam. If the laser beam is moved the hole becomes egg shaped in cross-section. Metal at the front of the hole is vaporized and swirls round the wall to the back of the hole. The metal here is cooling down because the heat from the laser is being moved away and the vapour condenses to form a bridge between the components. If we do this along the line of a joint between two pieces of metal, the vapour which condenses at the back wall of the hole forms a bridge and we have a weld. This technique for welding is known as **keyholing** (Fig. 1.8).

Laser welding units are large and the operation needs to be mechanised; usually the workpiece is moved under the welding head (Fig. 1.9).

Laser welding is a relative newcomer in the field of welding but the principles of keyholing have been used for some time in electron beam welding.

Electron beam welding

Instead of light, we can use a beam of electrons, which are electrically charged particles. Just like light, the electrons can be concentrated into a small diameter beam and focused to a spot on the surface of the joint. Unfortunately, electrons do not travel very far in air so we have to do the welding in a box or chamber in which we have created a vacuum (Fig. 1.10).

Although this makes handling and moving the component more difficult it does offer considerable advantages. The surface of the component is not oxidised because all the oxygen is removed when we pump the air from the chamber to create the vacuum. With electron beam welding it is also possible to maintain a high degree of dimensional accuracy. These two factors mean that machined components can be welded and put straight into service. On the other hand, if we use an arc process for the manufacture of, say, a gear cluster for a car transmission we are faced with a costly postweld machining operation because it is difficult to control the shape and dimensions of arc welded joints to the limits required for precision components. Electron beam welding is particularly successful with expensive materials such as stainless steel and titanium (Fig. 1.11).

Fig. 1.9　Typical laser welding machine at The Welding Institute

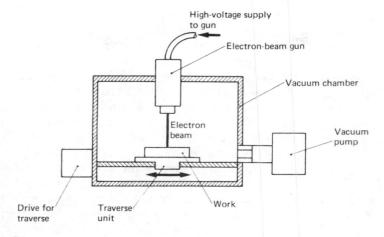

Fig. 1.10   Main components of an electron beam welding machine

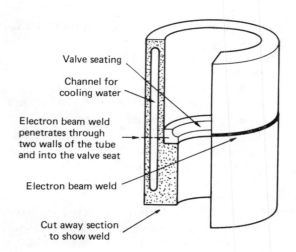

Fig. 1.11   Machined component welded by electron beam process

Friction welding

So far we have looked at welding techniques which involve melting. We also like to get away from molten metal if we can because it is often not easily controlled in the joint. It would be very useful if we could achieve bonding by just pushing the components together. In fact we can do this; for centuries, blacksmiths have welded bars by hammering them together – a **forge** or **pressure** weld. There are drawbacks, however. The metal has to be heated and considerable force needs to be exerted to make the bond. Pressure welding also involves changing the shape of the component at the joint.

A more up-to-date process which uses the principle of pressure bonding is friction welding (Fig. 1.12). If two pieces of metal are rubbed together, they become hot. An easy way to achieve this is to push two lengths of rod together, end to end, and rotate one of them (Fig. 1.12). If the relative movement is very fast – about 1500 revolutions per minute – it is possible to raise the temperature of the rubbing surfaces at the interface to near melting point. At this temperature the metal is plastic and the two bars can be pushed together, squeezing metal out from the interface. The result is a solid-to-solid pressure bond without any melted and solidified metal in the joint.

The metal which came from the interface forms a flash on the surface of the bar (Fig. 1.13). This can be removed by machining but in some applications it can be left in place without affecting the service performance of the joint.

Friction welding can be applied to a range of materials and is suited to joining different metals. This is not always possible with fusion welding because the mixture of the two metals may give a brittle weld which cracks apart on cooling. An example of this can be seen in any attempt to join aluminium to steel using MIG welding. With friction welding there is no molten metal left in the joint so the problem of cracking does not arise; aluminium can be welded to steel by this process.

The speed of rotation and the force applied to the joint in friction welding are determined by making trial welds. It is not suited, therefore, to one-off situations but is at its best on long production runs. Typical applications are adding high speed tips onto carbon steel shanks for drill bits, fixing flanges to tubes or pipes and attaching studs to plate surfaces, and back axle assemblies for cars.

Fig. 1.12 Large friction welding machine

Fig. 1.13   Friction welded stem for exhaust valve

In friction welding the hot metal must not be exposed to air because if it oxidises a bond cannot be formed. This means that with conventional techniques one component must be circular in cross-section; a square section would leave areas intermittently in contact with air. This is a major limitation to the use of the process. Techniques are being developed to enable square and irregular sections to be welded.

Which process?

The few examples of welding techniques quoted indicate the wide range of options available to the production engineer who wants to use welding as part of a manufacturing sequence. The choice of the best process is not always obvious. A number of factors must be taken into account; some of the most important are:

Technical suitability	Will it give the right type of weld?
	Is the metal suitable for welding?
	Will the joint have sufficient strength?
Economic aspects	How much will the weld cost?
	What capital investment is required?
	What effect does welding have on the cost of other operations?
Skill requirement	Does the effective use of the welding process depend on a high level of skill?
	Is this skill available?
	Can welders be trained?
Environmental problems	Are there operating hazards which require expensive safeguards?
	Will the workforce be exposed to health risks?

The answers to these and a host of other questions cannot be given for the whole range of processes in a short book. In the following pages we will be considering and explaining them in relation to fusion welding and in particular the manually operated processes which are widely used in industry and which are of interest to the DIY welder.

2

Arc Welding

When we were looking at examples of welding in Chapter 1, the point was made that there were many variations on the basic arc system.

Arc welding has been in use for over a hundred years. The first patent was taken out by a Russian named Benardos and his co-worker Olszewski in 1886. Their system was very crude and used a bare wire. Over the intervening period many developments have taken place, improving not only the quality of arc welded joints but also the ease of welding. In this chapter we will take a closer look at some of the more important arc welding processes.

Tungsten inert gas welding

We can make a start by examining a process which is widely used for the welding of sheet steel and aluminium, and butt joints in pipes. This process is known as tungsten inert gas welding, usually abbreviated to TIG. In some respects it is the simplest of the arc welding systems in that the heat from the arc is used to fuse the workpiece but the electrode is not melted. If extra metal is needed to build up the weld, as it would be for the fillet in a T-joint, it is added separately to the weld pool in the form of a thin wire. Melting of the electrode is avoided by making it from tungsten. This is a metal which has a melting point of about 3500°C. It is relatively easy to provide some additional cooling to conduct the heat away from the tip of the electrode and thus keep it below the melting point (Figs. 2.1, 2.2).

The weld pool, which is created by melting the parent material

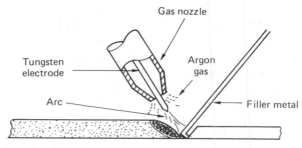

Fig. 2.1 Principles of TIG welding

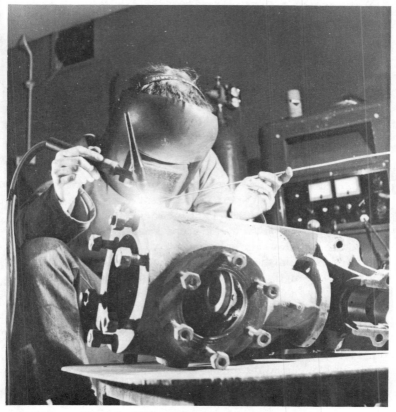

Fig. 2.2 TIG welding transmission housing

and possibly adding filler metal, would absorb oxygen and nitrogen if it was exposed to the air. This is undesirable because the dissolved gases might be released when the weld pool solidified and gas pores would be formed in the weld. This is known as porosity. Absorption of oxygen and nitrogen is avoided in TIG welding by surrounding the arc with argon, a gas that does not react with the molten metal. Such a gas is said to be **inert**; hence the inclusion of this word in the title of TIG welding. Argon is introduced to the arc area by a nozzle which is concentric with the electrode. The gas flows at a rate of 10 litres per minute which is enough to blow any air away from the vicinity of the arc. The nozzle is designed so that the blanket of gas covers not only the weld pool but also the solidified weld bead while it is cooling, leaving a clean, unoxidised surface to the weld.

There are three important variables in the welding operation which control the size of the molten pool and therefore the size of the weld. To some extent they also influence the quality of the finished weld. They are the arc length, the welding current and the speed at which the welder moves the electrode along the joint line. These are often referred to as the **welding parameters**.

Two of these parameters, current and travel speed, together determine how much heat is put into the weld. The current is set before welding commences and the level chosen depends on the thickness of the material being welded.

For most applications direct current (d.c.) is used. But when welding aluminium, an alternating current must be provided (see page 79). The current for welding is provided by a welding set or power source. The power source keeps the current at the level set by the welder but allows the voltage to vary to accommodate changes in the distance from the tip of the electrode to the surface of the weld pool – the arc length. The power source also contains a device which enables the welder to start the arc without needing to touch the electrode to the workpiece. If the tungsten electrode was brought into contact with the work, it would be contaminated and this would lower the melting point. The result would be that tungsten would be added to the weld pool and the electrode would be eroded.

The welder can adjust the arc length simply by moving the torch closer to or farther away from the workpiece. The arc length influences the width of the weld: the shorter the arc length the narrower will be the weld pool. Conversely, if the arc length is increased, in other words if the torch is moved away from the work, the weld pool increases in width. This means the welder can exercise a fine control over the size of the weld. Normally the arc length is between 1 and 3 mm and a considerable degree of skill is required to keep it constant along the length of a weld. Some idea of the difficulty that a welder faces in this respect can be obtained by simply holding a felt tipped marker pen above a sheet of paper and, without resting the hand, trying to move along a pencilled line keeping the tip of the pen 2 mm away from the surface. Observe how many times the pen makes a mark on the paper and then think that each touch-down would represent a contaminated weld.

Metal inert gas welding

Metal inert gas (MIG) welding was mentioned in Chapter 1 where we saw that it is widely used in the production of car bodies but also finds a use in the application of plates and pipes. Like TIG welding it uses a gas shield to protect the weld pool (Fig. 2.3).

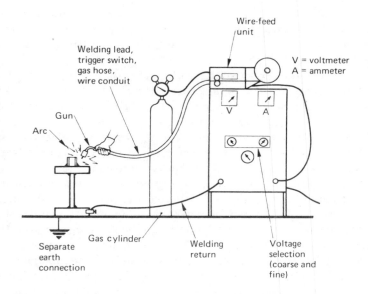

Fig. 2.3 Components of a MIG welding system

The important difference between MIG and TIG welding is that in the former the electrode is a wire of similar composition to the metal being welded. The wire melts in the arc and the molten droplets are added into the weld pool. This means that the wire must be driven or fed at the same rate that it is melting back to keep the arc length constant. The wire has a small diameter, somewhere between 0.8 and 1.6 mm according to the current being used. It melts at a rate of between 2.5 metres/min (100 in/min) and 9 metres/min (350 in/min). It is impossible for a welder to feed the wire by hand at this rate so a drive is incorporated into the system which pushes the wire along a hose and through the gun into the arc area. A particularly important feature of MIG welding is that the arc length is not controlled by the welder but is maintained at a pre-set level by the equipment. A power source for MIG welding is specially designed to supply direct current at a constant voltage. The voltage is selected by the welder to fix the arc length at the desired value. The current is controlled by adjusting the wire feed speed. The higher the speed, the greater the current that is drawn from the power source.

In many ways MIG welding is easier to use than TIG welding. Less skill is required to control the arc length as it is only necessary to hold the torch at a reasonably constant distance from the surface of the weld pool. Slight variations of 3 mm or so in the distance from the nozzle to the surface of the work can be compensated for by the power source. The skill in the process lies in directing the arc to get the best fusion of the work and adjusting the travel speed to ensure that the correct size of weld is produced.

The shielding gas deserves special mention. Argon is used for aluminium and stainless steel. The gas is inert, as we saw when we were looking at TIG welding, and does not react with the metal but effectively excludes oxygen and nitrogen from the atmosphere. For mild steel, however, carbon dioxide can be used either by itself or mixed with argon. Carbon dioxide (CO_2) is not inert in the chemical sense but in the arc it decomposes to give carbon monoxide which will not react with the steel being welded. You will probably know that we get carbon monoxide in the exhausts from cars and that it is poisonous. Fortunately, in MIG welding the small amounts of carbon monoxide produced by the decomposition of the shielding gas in the arc area burn in contact with air and revert to carbon dioxide which is safe. Welders can therefore use MIG welding without getting poisoned. Carbon dioxide is cheaper than argon and this is one of its attractions but it also confers different operating characteristics on the arc. In Chapter 8 we will be looking at the factors which would affect the choice between carbon dioxide or a mixture of this gas with argon for the welding of steel sheet and plate.

At this point, it is worthwhile looking at the names used for MIG welding. MIG is a shortened version of metal *inert* gas welding so it is clearly wrong to apply the name to the CO_2 shielded version. Both CO_2 and argon-CO_2 mixtures are active gases. To be logical we should use MAG – metal *active* gas welding. Other names have been used which are equally satisfactory, e.g. MAGS (metal arc gas shielded) and GMAW (gas metal arc welding). In this book we will use MIG/MAG to cover general points and MIG or MAG when referring to specific applications.

In general the electrode used for MIG/MAG welding is a solid wire but flux-cored versions are available for use on steel and for depositing a layer of hard, wear-resisting metal on the surface of, say, an excavator. Wires have also been developed where the flux core generates its own shielding gas, so there is no need to have an additional shield of CO_2 or argon-CO_2. These are known as self-shielded wires and are becoming much more common in their use in MAG welding.

Manual metal arc welding

Manual metal arc (MMA) welding is the oldest of the arc processes. It has been known by a variety of names and you may be more familiar with the term **stick electrode** welding. Often it is simply called electric welding but in the United States it is shielded arc welding (Fig. 2.4).

MMA uses a metal rod as an electrode. The rod is coated with a flux. Both the core wire (rod) and flux are melted by the arc (Fig. 2.5). The diameter of the core wire ranges from 2.4 mm to 6 mm, so the melting is slower than in MIG welding. An MMA electrode is usually 450 mm long, but the welder can only use 400 mm of it. The remainder is the stub-end which fits into the holder and is discarded. It takes between 2 and 3 minutes to melt a 400 mm length of

Fig. 2.4   Manual metal arc welding a thick test plate

electrode. This gives a melting rate of 130 to 200 millimetres per minute which is appreciably slower than the 2.5 to 9 metres per minute we observed in MIG welding. The significance of this slower melting rate is that the welder can look after the feed rate and hence we return to a situation where the welder is controlling the arc length. We need a similar power source to TIG welding, i.e. constant current, but there is no need for an arc starting device. The welder simply scratches the tip of the electrode along the joint line just as if striking a match. In fact the technique is known as **striking the arc**.

The weld pool is protected against atmospheric contamination by a slag which is produced by melting the flux covering on the electrode. The flux melts in the arc to form a liquid which covers the weld pool like a blanket. When this slag has solidified it

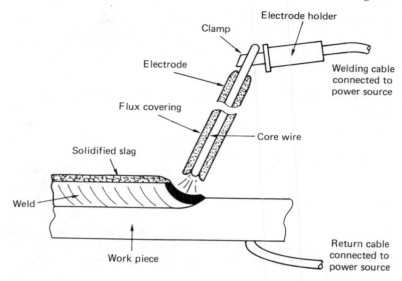

Fig. 2.5 Principles of manual metal arc welding

is removed from the weld by the welder using a chipping hammer.

Although the prime purpose of the flux is to provide protection against atmospheric contamination, it also performs other very important functions:

From the welder's point of view, perhaps one of the most important aspects of the flux is that it can contain chemical compounds which improve the ease of striking and controlling the arc.

Secondly it helps to support the weld. The solidification temperature for the slag depends on its composition. By using the right combination of chemical compounds in the flux, the slag can be made to solidify before the weld metal; in this way it forms a mould around the weld pool which is particularly valuable when welding a joint that is vertical. The flux also controls the profile of the weld. Some fluxes produce welds which have a very smooth finish and blend in at the edges of the weld. Others have more of a dome-shaped finish, perhaps with marks on the surface called rippling.

Finally the flux provides a means of adding alloying elements to the weld metal. The core wire of an electrode is always chosen to be similar to the material that is being welded. But to make it easier to manufacture electrodes, some of the chemical elements which are needed in the metal to give particular properties like strength or corrosion resistance are added to the flux. These mix with the weld pool when the flux and core wire melt. In the case of mild steel we would expect to see elements such as manganese, which gives added strength, and silicon, which removes oxygen from the weld pool and so minimises the risk of porosity. Similarly with stainless steel, chromium and nickel are added to the metal to give the proper corrosion resistance. These would be in the flux in the form of powders known as ferrochrome and ferronickel.

It can be readily seen, then, that there is not just one electrode for MMA welding. By blending the flux a wide variety of electrodes can be produced and in one manufacturer's catalogue there are no fewer than forty-five different electrodes to suit different materials and different welding applications. The selection of the best electrode is not an easy task and later in Chapter 9 we will be considering some of the more commonly used electrodes for the welding of steel.

Stud welding

So far in this chapter we have looked at the three principal manual arc welding systems. These are responsible for the bulk of the manual welding which is done on sheet, plate and other structures. Over the years there have been many variations on the three principal processes. Often they have been developed to meet a specific requirement. A good example of this is stud welding where the principles of arc welding have been adapted to making attachments to flat surfaces.

Frequently it is necessary permanently to fix a stud to either sheet or plate or section. The stud may be a bolt or threaded bar to which other components are temporarily attached. Alternatively the stud may be a fastener or hook or simply a locating device. Small studs going onto thin sheet are best fixed by resistance welding but where the base is a plate appreciable power has to be used to give a firm attachment. Very large studs can be fillet welded into place but this is a time-consuming process and with studs of 18 mm diameter and below it is not always a satisfactory answer. For this reason a process called arc stud welding has been developed which operates on a semi-automatic basis.

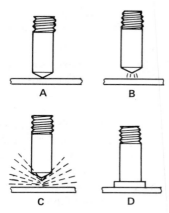

Fig. 2.6 Stud welding

The principles of stud welding are shown in Fig. 2.6. The end of the stud is shaped to a point and the tip is touched onto the plate surface (A). The stud is connected via the equipment back to the power source and the work is connected to the other terminal. The current is switched on and the tip of the electrode heats up due to resistance heating at the junction. As soon as the tip of the stud approaches melting point it is moved away from the surface and an arc is established (B). The arc melts the surface of the plate forming a weld pool and at the same time fuses the end of the stud (C). After a predetermined time the stud is plunged into the weld pool, the current is switched off and the metal solidifies to give a permanent bond between the stud and the plate (D). The weld metal is contained in place by a ceramic collar which is fitted around the outside of the stud. This also provides some protection against atmospheric contamination.

In operation, the stud is held in a special gun which is fitted with three prods. These enable the welder to position the gun correctly and to keep the stud in the right alignment during the welding sequence. Within the gun is a spring loaded actuator and the control can be programmed to ensure the correct sequence of events.

With this process studs need not be round. They can be flat strips or hexagonal bars. The finished length of the stud can be adjusted by altering the time the arc is operating.

Automation in arc welding

Manual arc welding is a skilled craft. Often the skill of the welder is essential in the welding of complex joints. It is also possible for one welder to tackle a variety of jobs using the same equipment. Manual arc welding tends to be slow, however, and the length of time which the arc can be run is restricted by the physical endurance of the welder. In MMA welding a further determining factor is the length of the electrode. Every three minutes or so the welder stops to insert a new electrode into the holder and the overall efficiency of the operation is reduced.

The length of time the arc is operating expressed as a percentage of the total time the welder is on the job is called the duty cycle. In MMA welding, duty cycles of the order of 20% are more or less the norm. With MIG/MAG welding it is possible to improve the duty cycle to around 30% to 35%. Occasionally, in long production runs on straight joints, duty cycles can be pushed up to as high as 60% but this tends to be the exception. Where the joint is straight, either on a flat surface or round a pipe, and there is little interference from neighbouring attachments, it is attractive to use a mechanised welding system which can weld for longer periods without stopping, at higher currents and at higher travel speeds. In this way significant increases in duty cycle can be achieved.

Submerged arc welding

The most widely used mechanised arc process is submerged arc welding (SA). As the name implies the arc is submerged but in this case under a layer of flux (Fig. 2.7).

The arc is struck between the end of a continuous wire electrode similar to that used in MIG welding, but the electrode diameter is appreciably larger, typically 4 to 6 mm. The arc length is automatically adjusted by altering the wire feed rate. Once a suitable speed has been selected, an electronic governor keeps the setting constant. Meanwhile the current is controlled by the power source.

The arc melts the flux surrounding it to form a slag which protects the pool and gives the surface its characteristically smooth finish. Although we cannot see the arc it behaves in a very similar way to MIG welding, but as a consequence of operating at higher currents (between 500 and 1000A) appreciably larger weld pools are pro-

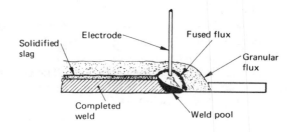

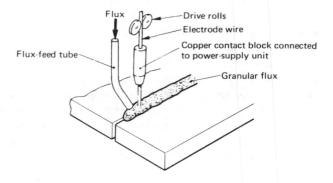

Fig. 2.7 Principles of submerged arc welding

duced. For this reason submerged arc welding is mainly used in joints where the weld metal is held in place by gravity. SA welding would not, therefore, be used to weld a joint which is vertical such as a butt in the side of a ship, otherwise the metal would run out of the groove.

The flux in the SA process, unlike MMA welding, does not normally contain large amounts of alloying elements as it is difficult to regulate the amount that is melted. The alloying elements are included in the wire which therefore has to be of a different composition for each of the different types of steel or stainless steel that can be welded.

When the welding has been completed unused flux is collected using a vacuum system and is recycled. The slag which has been formed detaches easily to reveal a very smooth surface profile.

Robots for welding

Welding robots were first used on volume production lines in the manufacture of cars and domestic appliances such as washing machines. Initially, most of the installations were for resistance spot welding which is ideally suited to mechanisation. The welding cycle in this process is electronically controlled and there is no need to move the electrodes while the weld is being made.

Robots are now more frequently used in general fabrication. A welding robot is in essence a manipulating device which simply moves the welding torch along the joint line thus performing some of the functions of the human welder. The main arc welding systems used with robots are TIG and MIG/MAG.

At present, three types of robot are in use for welding. The first is similar to the gun and turret mechanism of an army tank (Fig. 2.8a). The turret rotates thus altering the direction of the arm which can also be moved in and out or up and down. By combining these movements the gun can be made to follow the joint line.

A second and perhaps simpler type of robot has a base and a vertical column which moves from side to side and an arm which goes up and down or in and out (Fig. 2.8b). This gives three directions of movement similar to the sides of a box and is often called a Cartesian coordinate machine.

The most versatile welding robot is the jointed arm machine in which the movements of a welder's arm are simulated (Fig. 2.8c). There are pivots in the shoulder, elbow and wrists which give an infinite number of gun positions.

The robot needs to be told what to do and so a full system would not only have the mechanism for moving the gun but also requires a control unit which:

- controls how far the nozzle is from the work,
- alters the direction the nozzle is pointing,
- controls how fast the gun is travelling,
- sets the wire feed speed, and
- instructs the power source to deliver the correct current or voltage.

Welding robots are at their best on simple joints where it is easy to programme the path. The cost savings become most apparent when there are many of the same component to be welded because

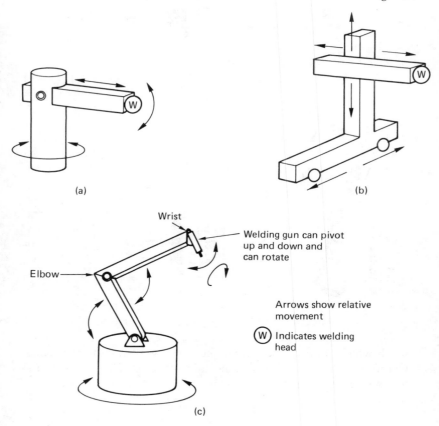

Fig. 2.8 Types of robot used for welding

programming the robot takes an appreciable time. It is worth bearing in mind that robots do not necessarily work faster than human beings. Their great asset is that they can continue working at the same speed when human beings would become tired and successful robotic applications are frequently designed on twenty-four hours a day operation. The other important attraction of robotics is that of reproducibility. Having set up the conditions and having obtained an accurate and reproducible joint assembly, the

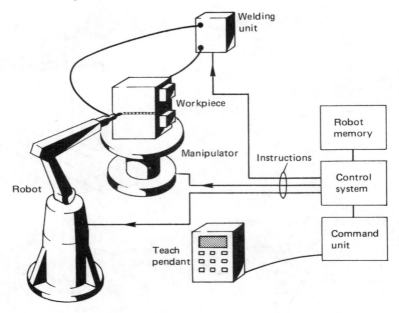

Fig. 2.9 Control system for a welding robot

welds which are produced should be consistent from the beginning to the end of a shift. This cannot always be guaranteed where a human welder is operating the gun.

3

Making a Weld

Now that we have seen some of the characteristics of arc welding processes we can choose the method which is best suited to the particular application we have in mind. Given the skill, we can go ahead and weld up the joint. However, if we really want good results we have to start a long way back, well before the arc is struck. In this chapter we will take a close look at the sequence which leads up to the assembly of the joint for welding and highlight some of the factors which have an important bearing on the quality of the final joint.

Design

We can start with the detailed design of the joint. The overall shape of the component or fabrication is decided by the designer in the light of service requirements. The position of the joint lines is dictated by changes in shape and also by the size of the material which is to be used. The unit may be assembled from plate, sheet, pipe or sections and in many ways the design is governed by what the steelmaker can supply. There are two further very important factors which should influence the positioning of a joint for welding, although very often these are overlooked.

Access to the joint
The first is concerned with access. The prime requirement for the production of a good quality joint is visibility. If the welder cannot see the joint clearly, it is unlikely that the arc can be directed into the joint line in such a way that the best fusion is achieved. The welder

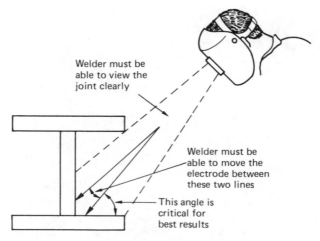

Welder must be
able to view the
joint clearly

Welder must be
able to move the
electrode between
these two lines

This angle is
critical for
best results

Fig. 3.1   Access requirements for welding a T-joint

also needs room to manoeuvre the arc. The angle between the
electrode and the joint surfaces is critical. Take for example a
T-joint. The tip of the electrode must be positioned at the root of the
T, but at the same time it needs to be moved from side to side to
direct the melting of the parent metal which is essential for bonding
between the molten weld pool and the surface of the plate. This is
illustrated in Fig. 3.1.

Joint thickness

Secondly there should not be too great a difference in thickness
between the two pieces making up the joint. If one member is much
thinner than the other, the welder has difficulty in directing the arc
to prevent melting through the thin member before sufficient heat
has built up in the thicker member to give fusion. This is particularly
a problem in T-joints where thin attachments such as lugs and
brackets are being welded to thicker plate – maybe a vertical column
or perhaps part of a tank structure.

We also have problems with butt joints. Where two plates of
unequal thickness need to be joined by a butt weld it is desirable that
the thicker plate should be tapered so that along the joint line it will
have the same thickness as the thinner plate.

Another example of a similar problem is TIG welding a pipe into

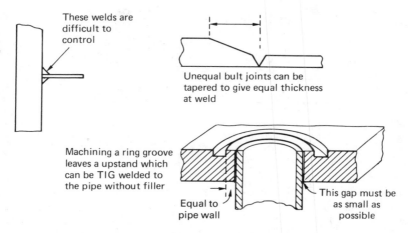

Fig. 3.2 Avoiding problems with unequal thickness

a plate. When the pipe has an appreciably thinner wall there is always the danger that it will be melted away before fusion has occurred in the plate. This can be alleviated by machining a ring groove in the surface of the plate around the hole.

Welding position

Thirdly we must take account of the position of welding. It is relatively easy to weld when the component is lying flat on the floor and the weld metal is held in the joint by gravity. It is a little more difficult when one plate in a T-joint is vertical and there is a tendency for the weld metal to run over the horizontal plate. With arc welding, the welder uses the force of the arc to keep the metal in place until the slag solidifies and forms a mould.

If the welded joint is vertical or overhead, the skill required to keep the metal in place increases and it becomes much more difficult to produce a satisfactory weld profile. It is also necessary to have smaller weld runs since the large weld pools, which we can use in the flat position, would just collapse and fall on the welder as droplets of molten metal.

The various positions of welding are given standard names so that we can readily recognise them. In America, however, the welding positions are identified by a number.

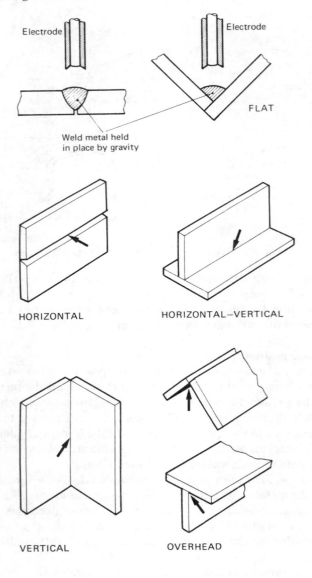

Fig. 3.3 Positions of welding

Edge preparation

The arc may look fierce but in reality it can only penetrate small distances into a piece of metal. For a butt joint to be successful it must be fused through the complete thickness of the joint line. There is, therefore, a major limitation on the use of a square edge; the maximum thickness depends on the process:

TIG ....2 mm
MMA welding.........................3 mm
MIG/MAG welding, low current ....3 mm
MIG/MAG welding, high current ....6 mm
SA welding ....10 mm

Fig. 3.4   Square-edge butt-welded joints

With thicker material we can turn the plate over and weld from the other side. If the gap between the edges is 2 to 3 mm we should be able to double the thicknesses given above. Beyond this we would end up with an area in the centre of the joint which would not be fused. The answer to this problem is to cut the edges back to form a V-shape and to fill the groove so formed with weld metal.

The first run into the V-shape is the root run. This calls for the highest degree of skill since there is always the danger that the weld pool will get too large, melt completely through the root faces and collapse on the underside. On the other hand, if insufficient heat is supplied to the joint, perhaps because the welder travels too fast in an attempt to avoid weld pool collapse, the root faces will not be fused properly and a poor quality weld results. In an acceptable weld, the root run should form a bead about 2 to 3 mm high on the underside of the joint – the penetration bead.

Sometimes it is possible to support the underside of the root run by using a backing bar or a backing strip. A backing bar is usually

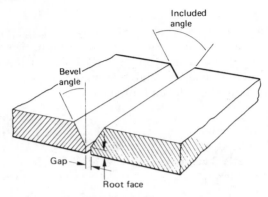

Fig. 3.5 Single-V preparation

made from copper and has a groove to form a mould for the weld metal which penetrates through the root. The backing bar is removed from the joint after the welding has been finished. A backing strip is made from the same material as the component we are joining and remains as a permanent part of the joint because the weld metal fuses into it.

Once the root run has been deposited, the groove is filled using a number of weld runs (filling passes). Finally the weld surface is built to the correct profile by depositing a capping pass. With this pass the welder may need to use a side-to-side movement to spread the weld metal across the top of the preparation. This weaving motion is common to many welding operations and the pattern used varies according to the welder's skill and the type of joint. In the flat position the weave tends to be in the form of a zig-zag moving from side to side. The welder hesitates momentarily at the sides of the weld to make sure that the parent metal is properly fused. With joints in the vertical position, whether they be butt or T, the weaving motion is in the form of a triangle, again with pauses at the edges of the weld to ensure fusion.

A single V-preparation is used on material up to about 12 mm thick. Above this thickness the width of the groove begins to get quite large and the amount of metal needed to fill it increases significantly. For thick plate, a double-V is preferred so that the weld is done from both sides. The amount of weld metal used is also less; as an example, with 18 mm plate the volume of weld metal in a

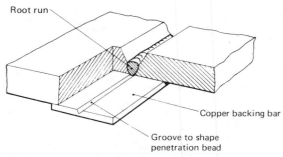

Root run

Copper backing bar

Groove to shape
penetration bead

(a) Temporary backing bar, with groove, to
support root run (removed after welding)

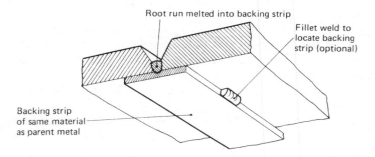

Root run melted into backing strip

Fillet weld to
locate backing
strip (optional)

Backing strip
of same material
as parent metal

(b) Permanent backing strip

Fig. 3.6 Temporary and permanent backing for butt welds

single-V is twice that which we would have to deposit for a double-V. When the thickness exceeds 30 mm it is quite common to use a U-preparation. This again helps to reduce the volume of weld metal required, but is appreciably more expensive to machine than the V-preparation.

There is a variety of ways of cutting the edge of the plate to provide a V-preparation. These range from using a hand file for small pieces of plate and the ends of pipe to more sophisticated machining methods with either a planer or a milling machine. Perhaps the most widely used method of edge preparation on plates is oxy-fuel gas cutting. This technique is considered in more detail in Chapter 10 when we discuss oxy-fuel gas systems.

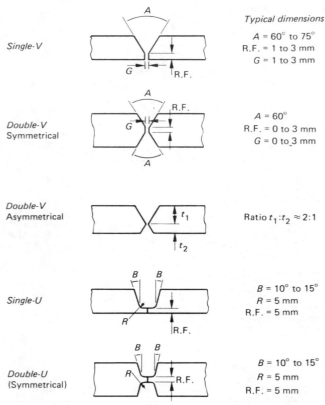

Single-V

Typical dimensions

A = 60° to 75°
R.F. = 1 to 3 mm
G = 1 to 3 mm

Double-V
Symmetrical

A = 60°
R.F. = 0 to 3 mm
G = 0 to 3 mm

Double-V
Asymmetrical

Ratio $t_1:t_2 \approx 2:1$

Single-U

B = 10° to 15°
R = 5 mm
R.F. = 5 mm

Double-U
(Symmetrical)

B = 10° to 15°
R = 5 mm
R.F. = 5 mm

Fig. 3.7   Typical edge preparations for butt joints

Distortion

All the commonly used metals expand when they are heated and contract or shrink on cooling. Without realising it we often depend on this change in dimensions in familiar everyday products. The thermostat which is used to control many domestic appliances relies on the fact that different metals expand at different rates. A common technique for loosening a nut which has become too tight to undo is to heat it with a blow torch. The expansion and contraction here will often break the seal along the line of the thread so that the nut can be more easily removed with a spanner. There are of course examples where expansion causes problems. Running a car

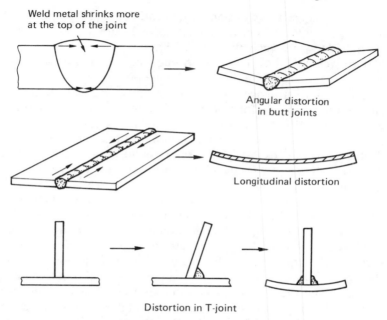

Weld metal shrinks more at the top of the joint

Angular distortion in butt joints

Longitudinal distortion

Distortion in T-joint

Fig. 3.8 Examples of distortion in welded joints

engine after all the water has leaked from the radiator leads to overheating with the result that the metal parts expand. The cylinder head may distort or warp, and the pistons may seize in the cylinders.

Contraction in welded joints

In welding, allowances must be made for the effects of contraction when the joint is cooling after the molten metal has solidified. Metal expands and shrinks in all directions but for the moment we can consider shrinkage in one direction only when we look at the cross-section of a V-joint which has been welded. For simplicity let us assume that the whole cross-section of the V is hot at the same time, although as we saw above it may be made up of a number of runs so the heating and cooling process is repeated. As the weld metal cools down, it tries to contract and exerts a pull on the parent metal on either side of the joint. The parent metal is cold and does not easily change its dimensions. On the other hand, the weld metal needs to occupy a smaller volume or shorter length so the two plates are pulled towards each other (Fig. 3.8).

If the weld is of the same width through the thickness of the plate, all we see is a change in the overall dimension of the component. This is called shrinkage and there are guide lines which enable allowance to be made for this change in dimensions when marking up the plates. But, the width of weld metal in a V-joint is greater at the top than at the bottom. There is more shrinkage at the top and the plates are pulled closer together than at the bottom. The result is that they appear to rotate about the root run to give angular distortion.

We can see similar effects of shrinkage in the longitudinal direction of the weld. We will assume that the whole length of the weld is hot to make it easier to explain the events. During cooling from the solidification temperature, one metre of weld metal would try to shrink by 25 mm in length. The weld is stopped from doing this by the presence of the rigid plates on either side. The weld metal is stretched and the actual reduction in joint length is only about 2 mm. At the same time, stresses are set up in the plates to resist the contraction of the cooling weld metal. As a result, the plates are bowed in the longitudinal direction.

T-joints also suffer distortion. The contraction which takes place across the face of the weld pulls the vertical member of the joints towards the horizontal one, so closing down the angle.

Controlling distortion

In making the weld we cannot avoid contraction – it is an essential property of all the commonly welded metals. So, we have to devise weld sequences which balance the contraction to ensure that the joint finishes with the required shape. In the transverse direction in a butt joint the plates can be pre-set in the opposite direction to the way in which they will be pulled during welding. It is also possible to hold the plates down with clamps but this requires considerable restraining force and may lead to difficulties in removing the component from the clamp when it has cooled. We can offset transverse distortion in butt welds by welding alternately on each side using a double-V preparation. We have to remember here that the first pass, i.e. the root run, will always produce more rotation than subsequent runs because the plate is free to move. After the root run has been deposited there is less freedom for movement since the root run in effect locks the joint and offers appreciable resistance to further rotation.

Pre-setting can also be used for T-joints, although this may not always be a practical proposition. Successful results can often be obtained by welding on both sides of the T, alternating runs from one side to the other.

In the longitudinal direction the shrinkage is accumulative. The weld does not cool at once as we suggested in our theoretical model. The arc travelling along the joint causes each point in the length to go through a heating and cooling cycle. At each point, therefore, a small amount of contraction is produced. This happens progressively along the joint and the result is a bow in the plate. On the other hand, if we weld only a short length at a time the bowing can be localised and the overall effect is a flatter plate. It is very difficult to predict the best sequence from theoretical considerations and the optimum results are obtained from experiment and experience. Many welders devise their own skip or step sequence by trial and error (Fig. 3.9).

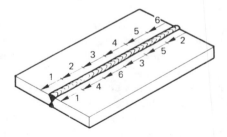

Fig. 3.9 Sequences for welding short lengths of a joint to prevent longitudinal bowing

In general terms for transverse shrinkage, the ideal is to have a parallel-sided weld. This is not easy to achieve with arc welding although the U-preparation in thick plates does approach it. The best process for the control of distortion is electron beam welding which we looked at in Chapter 1. Keyholing gives a parallel-sided weld of very small width (Fig. 3.10). This represents the optimum

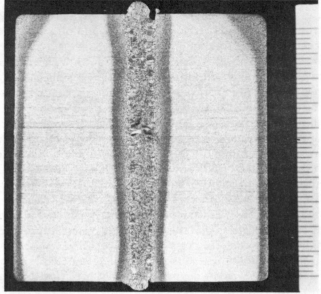

Fig. 3.10 Macrosection of an electron beam weld showing uniform width through the cross-section

condition to minimise transverse shrinkage and change of dimensions, and is one of the reasons why electron beam welding can be used on finished machined components which can be put into service directly from welding.

If arc welded components need to be machined to size, any cutting must be done after the welding operation. Often such machining releases locked-up stresses which have been induced in the weld during cooling and these can lead to further changes in dimension during the cutting operation. Where finished dimensions must adhere to close tolerances it is often the practice to heat-treat the component to relieve (release) the stresses. The precise details of the heat treatment depend on the metal; guidance is contained in standards such as BS5500. For the type of carbon steels used in general fabrication a typical treatment would be to heat the component slowly in a furnace or oven to a temperature of about 600°C, hold at this temperature for one hour while the stresses are removed and then cool slowly in the oven to avoid setting up new stresses.

Assembling the joint

For the best result in welding the joints must have good fit-up. With butt joints, the plates or pipes must be in line at the root and the root gap must be uniform along the length of the joint. The root faces should be of constant dimensions otherwise the welder will have difficulty in controlling the amount of melting required to get good penetration. For T-joints the main consideration in fit-up is the maintenance of a uniform gap along the joint line.

In practice it may be necessary to carry out some local grinding to match the joints completely. Variations in the profile of the cut edge may have occurred as the result of poor machining practice, but often misalignment is a direct result of the tolerance in the dimensions of the material which we are welding. Steel plates on delivery may well be bowed. If we take a straight-edge along a large plate the centre can be as much as 4 to 5 mm lower than the outer edges. Placing a vertical member onto this to form a T-joint results in no gap at the edges and a large one in the centre. Whilst the welder can accommodate gaps up to 3 mm, it is a greater problem to have to deal with one which varies along the length, as this means that travel speed, arc length and electrode angle must be continually changed to achieve fusion and a uniformly sized weld pool. Similarly, pipes and tubes are rarely truly circular in cross-section. Most manufacturing standards allow a degree of ovality and during the assembling of a joint for a butt weld it is usually necessary to rotate the pipes to get the best match.

The simplest way of holding the joint together is to deposit short lengths of weld either in the root or on the reverse side. These are called tack welds and are normally between 12 and 25 mm long. The spacing between tack welds depends on the length of the joint and the thickness of the parent metal. As a general guide, a tack weld should be placed at intervals of not less than 20 times the thickness of the material. So with 3 mm (10swg) sheet, tack welds would be about 12 mm long spaced at 60 mm intervals. The tack welds must be made to a high standard. It is a common fallacy that faults and defects in tack welds can be melted out when the full weld is made. This is not true and many service failures of welded joints have been traced back to bad tack welding. Care must also be taken to fuse the weld run into the surface of the tack weld. On some high quality

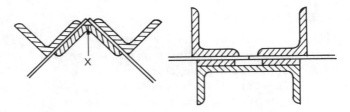

Fig. 3.11 Simple methods of clamping flat and corner sheet metal joints to maintain edge alignment and reduce distortion; to provide a gap under joint in corner joint, edge of angle should be removed, as at X

work, it is practice to grind away each tack in turn as the weld is deposited, to minimise the risk of faults being left in the finished joint.

The joint can also be held in alignment by clamps. For sheet welding, especially where large numbers of welds are to be made, it is useful to make a clamp of the type shown in Fig. 3.11. For small components, G-clamps and similar devices are adequate. This is common practice in pipe welding and a number of specially designed clamps are available for this application (Fig. 3.12).

The final operation in assembling the joint is to clean the weld faces thoroughly to remove grease, rust, oxide scale and so on. These contaminants lead to the formation of gas bubbles which are trapped in the weld as porosity. They can also make it more difficult to get good fusion.

Welding procedure

At last we are ready to start depositing the weld itself. At various points in our discussion so far we have indicated some of the choices that have to be made. Firstly there is of course the process. Then having selected the most appropriate process available, we have to decide on the electrode, shielding gas or flux. We also need to choose the level of current for welding since this dictates the diameter of electrode which we require. The current varies from the root run to the filling passes to the capping pass and the choice is made in accordance with the requirements of each type of run.

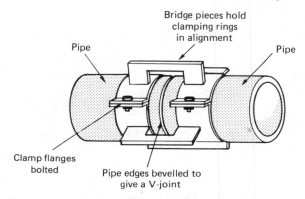

Fig. 3.12   Pipe clamp used to align joint for tacking (removed before welding)

We have also seen the need to balance welding about the joint to minimise the levels of distortion. Finally it may be necessary to heat the plates during welding to avoid cracking problems. This is particularly relevant to higher strength steels and cast iron and we will be studying this in more detail in Chapter 5.

All this information can be collected together onto a welding procedure sheet so that the welder can always have to hand details of the optimum procedure for a particular joint. A typical welding procedure sheet is shown on p. 48.

Welding Procedure — Manual Welding

Order No: 19671/PW/87	Drawing No: WS/19671/06885-03	Welder: Z. Clarke	Works No: 687
Sheet No: WP14	Joint Reference: WP14/1 to 7	Process (es): TIG — root run MMA — fill	

Joint Preparation:	Welding Sequence:
Cleaning Method: Vapour degrease	Material: BS4360 Grade 50D Pipe
	Gouging Method: N.4.

Welding Parameters

Electrode	Filler Wire	Pass No	Elect size mm	Filler diam. mm	Pos'n	Amps	Volts	Wire Feed Speed max/min	Travel Speed max/min
1.1% Thoriated	BS2901 A	1	3.2	2.4	Fixed hor.	90 to 110	—	—	—
2 ⎫ 3 ⎬ E5133B14H 4 ⎭ Xytrode		2	2.5	—	Fixed hor.	70–80	—	—	—
Store in ovens at 150°C	Shielding Gas	3	3.2	—	Fixed hor.	110–125	—	—	—
	Composition: Argon	4	3.2	—	Fixed hor.	110–125	—	—	—
	Pressure: 2.2 bar Flow rate: 7 l/min								

Preheat:
   Root run - none
   2, 3, 4 – 75°C
	Inspection

	Standard:	Method

Preheat: Root run - none 2, 3, 4 – 75°C	Inspection	
Interpass Temperature: 95°C minimum 5°C maximum	Standard: Client's spec	Method Visual ☑ Radiography ☑ Ultrasonic ☐
Post Heat: None	Insp. Authority: Client's representative	Dye pen ☑ Mag part ☐

Notes: Root run (1) is to be checked with dye pen before depositing run 2

Originator *Htm*	Checked S.Smith	Approved GtD	Date of Issue 28/6/89	Returned to File: 14/12/89	

4

What Makes a Good Weld?

'There's a good weld, look how smooth and flat it is.'
'That weld can't be strong enough, it's too flat. You need more
    reinforcement on top.'
'Welding up a crack makes the metal stronger.'
'Joints always break at the weld.'

These are four commonplace remarks. They are conflicting and
misleading, but each contains a grain of truth. They reflect the fact
that it is not easy to quantify a weld. We can see that a dovetailed
joint in wood is a tight fit and we know that it will have good
strength. A torque wrench gives us a measure of the tightness of a
bolted joint. But how do we decide if a weld is good?

First we need to ask ourselves what we mean by a 'good weld'.
The straightforward answer is that a good weld is one which is
acceptable for the application we have in mind. That may sound like
begging the question, but it is a very important concept.

Think about some typical examples:

At the top end of the quality scale we could look at a nuclear
containment vessel. If the weld in the steel plates which make up the
shell of the vessel were to fracture the result would be catastrophic.
The designer therefore sets a very high standard of integrity and
aims for a large factor of safety in the strength of any welded joints.

A quite different example would be a vat for brewing beer. Whilst
the welds must be strong enough to stop the walls of the vat from
falling apart, one of the main concerns is leaktightness. We cannot
afford to have voids (porosity) in the weld through which liquid
could escape. At the same time much thought must be given to the
problem of corrosion. During the fermenting process the liquid

would attack mild steel, so the vat is made from stainless steel. The weld metal must have as good a corrosion resistance as the plate material, otherwise there will be a leak at the joint.

We must not overlook the aesthetics of a welded component. The designer of a tractor works out the stresses in the joint and decides what the strength of the weld should be. But the specification may not stop there. It may be decided that some welds should have a smooth surface to give a pleasing appearance when the tractor has been painted. In this case a weld with pronounced ripples would not be acceptable even though the strength may be more than adequate.

Smooth weld surfaces may also be a critical requirement where fatigue loading is present. Fatigue of welded joints is a very important aspect of design and we will be looking at it in more detail later in this chapter.

So, we can see that different people have different interpretations of what is an acceptable weld. British Standards provide a good guide to acceptance criteria for a number of products and a list of the more common welding standards is given in Appendix A. But note, these standards do not imply that we can set out to produce a weld containing defects. The aim must always be to deposit the best weld possible; it does not cost any more to make a good weld in the first place. What the standard is telling us is that if we do get some defects it may not be necessary to go to the expense of cutting the weld out and starting again. It all depends on the application.

Strength of welded joints

In the examples of what makes a good weld, we have used the term *strength* quite loosely. Mostly when we talk of strength we are really referring to the tensile properties of the weld. One way of understanding these properties is to look at what happens to a strip of metal when it is stretched in a tensile test.

Fig. 4.1 shows a strip of steel clamped at one end to a solid block. The other end is gripped by a clamp. A pull or force applied to the clamp by means of the screw starts to stretch the metal as if it were a piece of elastic. The steel only stretches by a small amount, say 0.5 mm. If the end of the strip is released, it returns to its original length. In other words it behaves elastically. But, suppose we increase the force to a higher level by turning the screw a little more.

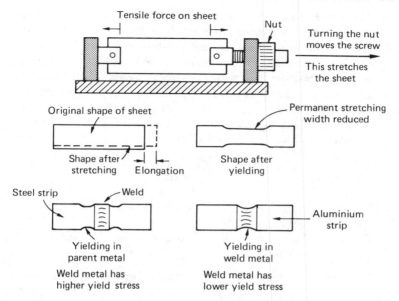

Fig. 4.1 Tensile behaviour of unwelded and welded sheet

The strip would get longer but would still return to its original length if we released the clamp. We can repeat this operation, turning the screw further each time to stretch the strip even more. However, a point is reached at which the steel does not return to its original length, i.e. it is permanently stretched. It has yielded and the force which has caused this is known as the **yield stress**.

The yield stress has an important role in design. No-one wants the steel frame of a building, or a car floor panel or any other welded product to change shape permanently every time it is used. So the designer has to ensure that the forces applied in service never take the steel above the yield stress. Fortunately, we can quantify the yield stress and we can usually discover the value for a particular metal from the supplier's specification or from a standard. For example, weldable steels are covered by British Standard BS970 or BS4360 whilst aluminium and its alloys are the subject of BS1470.

The yield stress is usually quoted as the force per unit area of cross-section. In countries which use the metric system, force is measured in Newtons. Alternatively, it can be given in tons or pounds. In Europe, the unit of stress is one Newton per square millimetre; this is shortened to N/mm^2. In the USA it is more often than not quoted in pounds per square inch (psi).

At this stage we do not need to worry too much about the precise meaning of these measurements of stress. We can simply use them as an index. For example, as a rough guide, we would expect that mild steel would have a yield stress of about 240 N/mm^2.

Using this figure, we can calculate the force needed to produce permanent stretching of our strip of steel:

First, we need to work out the area of the cross-section.
The strip is 25 mm wide and 1 mm thick.
The cross-section is therefore $25 \times 1 = 25$ mm^2.
Each square millimetre of cross-section can take a force of 240 Newtons before it yields.
Therefore the force needed to stretch the strip permanently is $240 \times 25 = 6000$ Newtons.

It is difficult to visualise 6000 Newtons, but in practical terms it means that a 25 mm wide strip of 1 mm thick steel could support the weight of seven people each weighing about 13½ stone, or 85 kg, before it starts to yield.

The designer usually works the other way round from this. Knowing the force which will be applied in service, the thickness of the steel is chosen so that the stress (N/mm^2) never exceeds, say, two thirds of the yield stress. This gives a factor of safety.

What happens when there is a weld across the width of the strip? In the elastic range, the weld makes no difference. It stretches by the same amount as the parent metal and returns to its original size if the force is removed. As we approach the yield point, we really want the parent material to be the first to go. In this way we know that the weld has no effect on our calculations. So, when we choose an electrode or filler wire, whatever the process, we ideally want it to give a weld with a higher yield stress than the parent metal. This is easy to do if the metal is steel. Unfortunately, with aluminium we usually find ourselves with welds which have a lower yield stress than the parent metal. We will look in more detail at the implications of this in Chapter 5.

If you think about this last paragraph you can see why there is some truth in two of the statements made at the beginning of the chapter. True, if the metal is steel and the right electrode is used, the weld metal is stronger than the parent metal, but all this means is that we do not need to alter our original design calculations. On the other hand, if the weld metal is weaker than the parent metal, building up the surface of the weld might just tip the balance by reducing the actual stress in the weld. Remember, stress is equal to the force divided by the cross-sectional area. Hence, the theory is that thickening up the joint increases the cross-section and gives a lower stress in the weaker weld metal. In practice the value of this approach is doubtful and there is always the risk that someone will grind off the build-up. The technique is sometimes called, quite wrongly, reinforcing the weld. The correct term for the metal piled on top of the weld is **excess metal** because it is in excess of requirements and costs extra money to deposit (Fig. 4.2). It is much better practice to design the joint on the yield strength of the weakest region whether it is the parent metal or the weld metal.

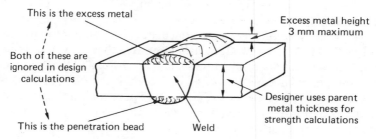

Fig. 4.2 Design features of a single V-butt weld

How does a welded joint fail?

It is very rare to find a welded joint that has failed because the stress exceeded the yield point of the parent metal. Normally, there are two main causes of failure:

- serious defects in the weld metal or in the parent metal along-side the weld;
- fatigue loading.

Effect of weld defects
Look at Fig. 4.3a on p. 55. This shows the cross-section of a butt joint which was welded from both sides. On the surface, the welds

looked satisfactory, but the section shows that the joint line has not been fused through the thickness. There is a **lack of penetration** and the cross-sectional area has been effectively reduced. Lack of penetration is one of the most common defects in welding and results from incorrect choice of welding conditions or from inadequate skill on the part of the welder.

Another common defect which can lead to a reduction of cross-section is **lack of fusion**. This can occur in the root of the joint, at the weld metal to parent metal interface or between weld runs (Fig. 4.3b). Almost invariably it results from incorrect welding technique. The solid metal must always be fused before the molten filler metal runs onto it.

Perhaps the worst type of defect is a crack. There is no single cause of cracks in welded joints. The reasons vary from one metal to another and some of the more important aspects are discussed in Chapter 5. For the moment we simply need to recognise that cracks can be formed in a joint during welding. Fig. 4.3c shows two types of crack which can occur in steel.

All three types of defect can reduce the joint's ability to carry the service loads and so produce a failure. Whether they will or not depends on a number of factors such as their size and location, and the service conditions. Mathematical techniques are available to assess whether the defect is significant. These tend to be complex and are only used for highly critical applications such as nuclear plant and oil platforms. More readily useful guidance can be obtained from British Standards and similar documents. As an example, BS5500 gives rules for the design of pressure vessels used in processing plants and power stations. It contains a section on the maximum allowable size for any defects discovered in the welds. Other British Standards relate to bridges, cranes, building frames and so on.

In general terms, cracks are never acceptable, but some lack of penetration or lack of fusion may be tolerated for less critical structures.

Fillet welds

When we were talking about lack of penetration, it might have occurred to you that a fillet welded T-joint has this defect built into it. So why are there not more failures in T-joints?

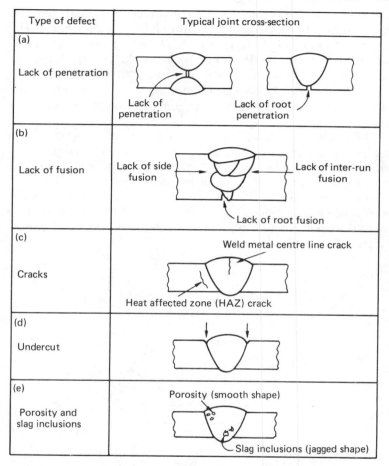

Type of defect	Typical joint cross-section
(a) Lack of penetration	Lack of penetration / Lack of root penetration
(b) Lack of fusion	Lack of side fusion / Lack of inter-run fusion / Lack of root fusion
(c) Cracks	Weld metal centre line crack / Heat affected zone (HAZ) crack
(d) Undercut	
(e) Porosity and slag inclusions	Porosity (smooth shape) / Slag inclusions (jagged shape)

Fig. 4.3 Typical defects in welds

The answer to this lies in the size of the weld. The section which carries the load is the **throat** (Fig. 4.4). The aim is to build up the size of the weld so that the throat is large enough to carry the load without yielding.

How then can the welder check that the throat is of the correct size? For convenience, we can think of the fillet weld in section as if it is a right-angled triangle. The throat is the shortest distance from the apex to the hypotenuse. This means that the length of one of the sides is equal to approximately 1.4 times the throat thickness. This measurement is called the **leg length** and can be easily checked by the welder. A useful rule of thumb when welding steels is that the leg length of the fillet in a double sided weld should be equal to the plate thickness, provided the correct strength electrode or filler wire has been used. Two ways of measuring leg length are shown in Fig. 4.5.

Did you notice that we have ignored the excess metal? Most fillet welds in practice have a convex surface which gives a larger throat than the measurement we have used. But it is difficult to control the amount of excess metal, so in design calculations it is ignored.

What about fillet welds with concave surfaces? These certainly look much neater, but the throat thickness has been reduced so the weld is weaker. In general, it is better to aim for a slightly convex fillet.

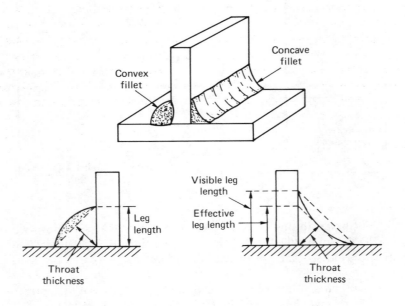

Fig. 4.4   Fillet weld details

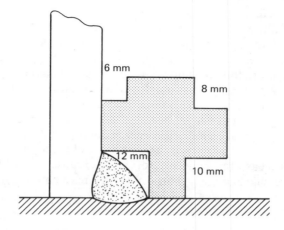

Fig. 4.5 Measuring leg length of a fillet weld

(a) Using a simple sheet metal gauge

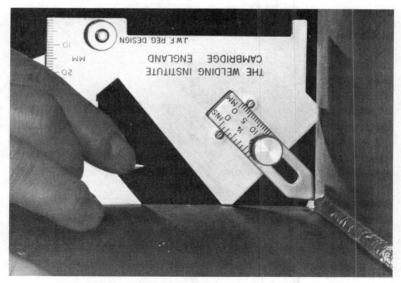

(b) Using a Welding Institute multi-purpose gauge

Fatigue loading

Fatigue failures in metal are not new. Engineers of the last century were familiar with breakages in connecting rods and carriage axles. In recent times, we have become only too aware of the problems associated with the formation of fatigue cracks in aircraft.

In many ways fatigue is an unfortunate term since the cracks are not the result of metal becoming tired. A fatigue crack starts at a point where there is a high, localised stress. This happens around a **notch** which might be a sharp corner, a deep scratch or a machining mark on a rotating shaft, or the toes of a weld in a joint (Fig. 4.6). These all act as stress concentrators and can cause a tenfold increase in the stress level at their sharpest point. This means that even with

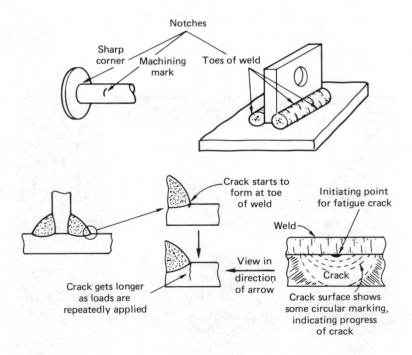

Fig. 4.6   Fatigue cracking in welded joints

applied loads well below yield, the tip of the notch may be taken above yield. If this occurs only once or twice there is probably not much cause for concern. But when the stress changes from a low to a high level many times, two things happen. First a small crack is formed or initiated at the point of stress concentration. From then on the crack is lengthened each time the stress is raised. Eventually, the crack progresses through the thickness of the component and there is a complete failure.

Welded joints are particularly prone to fatigue cracking because the junction of the weld and the parent metal at the surface, i.e. the toe, forms a notch which provides a site for a fatigue crack. Very often, in structures such as bridges, the welded joints are the first to show the effects of fatigue loading with cracks at the toes of the fillet welds in the flanges. This is what gives rise to the last of the quotations at the beginning of the chapter; it is a fact that if there is a fatigue failure, the joints crack at the edge of the weld. The aim of good design is to avoid a crack starting in the first place.

What type of welded structure is most likely to suffer from fatigue cracking? At the larger end of the scale, we might find fatigue cracks in the welded joints of bridges or crane girders or in parts of heavy vehicles such as bulldozers and excavators. The loads imposed on these are continually varying. A vehicle travelling across a bridge represents one cycle of stress for each axle. Similarly each load lifted by the crane or moved by the excavator generates an increase in stress at the joints. Fatigue cracks should not occur if the designer has allowed for the presence of varying stress levels and recognises the role of the welded joint.

Other common examples of welded items which are subjected to varying stress levels and therefore could suffer from fatigue cracking are:

- towing hooks for trailers
- brackets supporting chains on a child's swing
- lifting gear

If the welds are of good quality and of adequate size, these structures should not fail in service by fatigue. Unfortunately, in practice, conditions may be far from perfect. Overloading the structure shortens the life and leads to early failure. Both the lorry driver who carries overweight loads and the crane driver who exceeds the Safe Working Limit (SWL) contribute to fatigue failure.

Often the causes of a fatigue failure can be traced to welds which contain lack of fusion or penetration, cracks or undercut (see Fig. 4.3). A common situation where this occurs is in what is known as **casual welding**, for example, when brackets are added as an after-thought often in places where there is inadequate access and it is impossible to obtain good fusion or penetration. Structures which are subjected to fatigue must be inspected regularly and cracks should be repaired as soon as they appear.

Where there is a risk of fatigue failure, the life of the joint can be increased by grinding along the toe of the weld to give a smooth transition. This should not be overdone to the extent of reducing the thickness of the plate. But, grinding does *not* compensate for lack of fusion, cracks and the like. We must start with a good weld.

Checking weld quality

There are a number of defects which, if they are present, can be seen on the surface of a weld. Undercut, lack of penetration, poor profile and incorrect leg length (on a fillet weld) can all be detected by visual examination.

Many of the defects produced in a weld are internal. They are buried below the surface and cannot be detected by just looking at the weld. This means that for critical joints we need an inspection technique which can locate internal flaws. We can, of course, find a defect by cutting the weld open. If we are making a large number of welds we can select, say, every fiftieth component as a sample and examine it by sectioning to see if there are any defects in the weld. Unfortunately, this destroys the component and the technique is not feasible if we have only a small number of welds to examine. We need a non-destructive method of testing (NDT).

There are a number of NDT techniques available to the inspec-tor, but the two most commonly used to examine welds for internal defects are **radiography** and **ultrasonic testing**.

In principle, the first of these is similar to the technique used to X-ray people who have broken bones or suffer from chest com-plaints. The main difference is the power of the X-rays. To examine a weld they have to be strong enough to penetrate through the metal

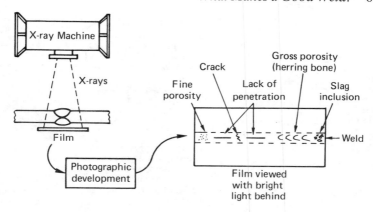

Fig. 4.7 Radiographic testing

and reach a photographic film which is fixed to the underside of the joint (Fig. 4.7). After the film has been exposed to the X-rays for a measured time, it is developed in the same way as a film used in a camera. If there are no defects the film shows a uniform density. The parent metal absorbs some of the X-rays, but we do not notice this because the absorption is the same across the whole of the section being examined. Defects like cracks, slag inclusions, gas pores and lack of penetration absorb less radiation than the metal, and show up as dark spots on the film. The radiograph, as the developed film is called, gives us a permanent record of the defects which we can study before deciding whether they are sufficiently bad to justify rejecting the weld.

Although radiography is a very useful and widely used method of NDT, it requires a lot of equipment and it poses safety problems. X-rays are hazardous and workers must be protected from the radiation. Either the component must be radiographed in a specially constructed room or chamber, or the area around the structure must be vacated by personnel. Anyone working with X-rays must wear a 'badge' which registers any exposure to X-rays.

A useful alternative to X-rays is ultrasonic testing (Fig. 4.8). In this method of NDT, a pulse of ultrasound is injected into the joint. The pulse travels through the metal until it meets a defect when some or all of the ultrasound is reflected back. The reflection or

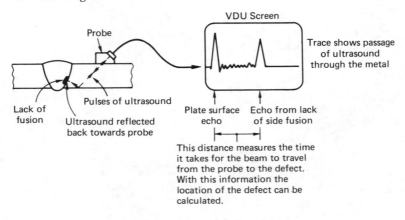

Fig. 4.8   Ultrasonic testing

echo is detected by a sensor and is displayed on the screen of a VDU. The method is portable, avoids the safety hazards of radiography and can detect very small defects. The drawbacks are that it requires a very high degree of skill to operate and it does not give a permanent record. Even so, it is widely used with success on critical structures such as pressure vessels, oil platforms and high pressure gas pipelines.

Making a test weld

Both radiography and ultrasonic testing are expensive not only in terms of the equipment required but also in the use of skilled operators. They can only be justified where high levels of integrity are required. In other cases we must rely on control of the welding operation. But this in turn depends on the use of a welding technique which we know can give good results. For many applications, especially those undertaken in the jobbing shop or for DIY purposes, we can start by establishing the procedure on a small test piece which can be tested destructively. Then we must pay particular attention to ensuring that the same procedure is used for the actual job.

The test weld need only be a few inches long, but the conditions must be carefully noted. The following should be recorded so that the weld can be reproduced if it is satisfactory:

- the edge preparation
- type and size of electrode or filler wire
- current or wire feed setting
- voltage (if a meter is fitted to the set)
- nozzle size (in oxy-acetylene welding)
- number and position of the weld runs
- leg length of fillet welds

Two pieces are cut from the weld as shown in Fig. 4.9, using a hacksaw. The first is fractured by hammering it in a vice – a saw-cut is made along the centreline of the surface of the weld to make it easier to break. The fractured surface is examined using a low power magnifying glass, preferably with a times three or four magnification. Lack of penetration or fusion, gas pores and slag inclusions can be seen on the fracture if they are present. Although this test is crude it is very useful within the range of thicknesses from 3 mm up to 12 mm. Below 3 mm the welds are too small to notch whilst if the metal is thicker than 12 mm the welds could be too tough to fracture by hammering. Within this range, if the weld does not break, it is a good one!

The second sample is used for a macrosection (Fig. 4.10). Special preparation facilities are needed to match the detail shown in the macrosections in this book, but adequate results can be achieved with simple techniques if we are only interested in the major features of a weld such as profile, position of individual weld runs and defects (Fig. 4.11). Macro-examination can be used on all thicknesses and provides an alternative to the fracture test, but it gives information about only one place in the weld. We may need to cut two or three sections spaced at intervals along the test weld if we are looking for defects.

The surface is prepared by rubbing on wet-and-dry paper until all deep scratches are removed. In this condition, it can be etched to reveal the weld structure by immersing the sample in dilute nitric acid (if it is mild steel) or caustic soda (for aluminium). *When etching, eye protection and rubber gloves must be worn.*

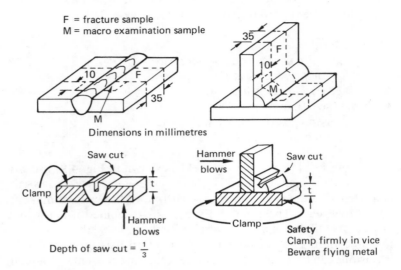

F = fracture sample
M = macro examination sample

Dimensions in millimetres

Examination of fracture test specimen

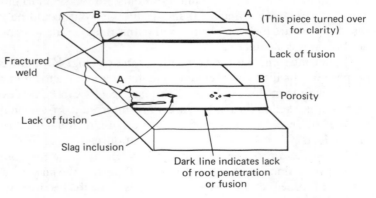

Fig. 4.9　Fracture tests on a sample weld

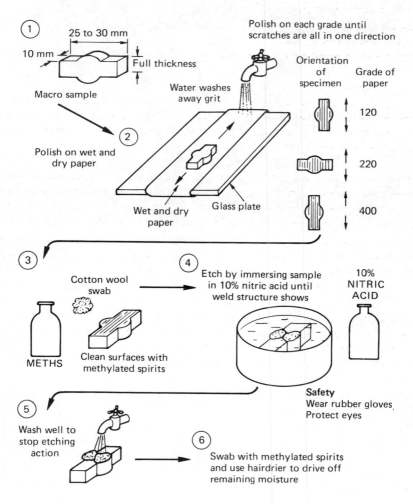

Fig. 4.10 Preparing a macrosection

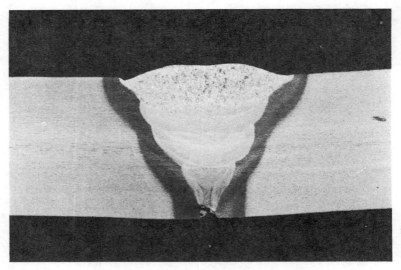

Fig. 4.11   Macrosection of multi-pass weld

The etched surface is examined with the aid of a times three magnifying lens to show the presence of cracks and other defects. The extent of the fusion into the parent metal can also be established.

5

Which Metal?

The most commonly welded metal is steel. It also happens to be the easiest to weld. Another metal which can be readily joined by welding is aluminium although it calls for more skill in controlling the weld pool than steel. Metals like copper, brass and cast iron can be welded but they require special techniques and skills to achieve satisfactory results.

Weldability

When we describe a metal as being weldable we need to define what we mean. In the previous paragraph we were commenting on the ease with which a weld can be deposited, but we might have said that steel is more weldable than aluminium because it is somewhat easier to make a weld. Both statements would be an incomplete account of the relative weldabilities of each metal. Weldability is a much wider concept which also embraces both the quality and properties of the joint.

There are a number of questions to be answered when making a complete assessment of weldability. Some of the most important are:

- Is the parent metal prone to cracking alongside the weld?
- Does the weld metal crack during solidification?
- What mechanical properties will the joint have?
- Will there be a risk of brittle fracture in service?
- Will the joint have acceptable corrosion resistance?
- Will there be a loss of electrical conductivity through the weld metal?

These are only some of the questions we may need to answer before tackling a joint. They can all be grouped together under the general heading of weldability.

In many ways weldability is a vague concept; we cannot define it in numerical terms. Sometimes the same metal can be judged to have both good and poor weldability according to the application we have in mind. A butt welded steel pipe may behave satisfactorily in a heating system; it can withstand the internal pressure of the steam and the joints do not leak. Steel therefore has good weldability in this application. But if the same pipe is used at sub-zero temperatures the joint may have low impact properties and there might be a risk of a fracture. In such a case, we would say that this steel has poor weldability.

A complete account of the weldability of the various commercially used metals requires a comprehensive understanding of all the service conditions and a knowledge of the metallurgy of the proposed joint. Such a study is outside the scope of this book but in this chapter we can highlight some of the more important practical aspects of weldability.

Heat affected zone

You might have noticed that we did not confine our thoughts about weldability to the weld metal. We extended it to include the whole of the joint because welding can have a dramatic effect on the parent metal.

When the arc has melted the parent metal and has been moved along the joint, the weld starts to cool. If the welding current is, say, 200A we are supplying about 2 kW of energy to every 10 mm length of joint which is equivalent to the heat given out by two bars of an electric fire. This is a large amount of heat concentrated into a small area. How does it escape when the weld is cooling? You might think that it is radiated from the surface. Well, a small amount does go this way but the majority flows through the parent metal. The consequence of this is that the metal on either side of the fusion boundary is first heated and then cooled as the heat flows out into the component. With most metals this brings about metallurgical changes. Some metals become softer whilst others may lose their corrosion resistance. Steel can also be hardened. The extent of these effects depends on the type of metal, the highest temperature reached and the speed or rate of cooling. The area of parent metal which undergoes a change in properties is called the **heat affected zone** – usually this is abbreviated to HAZ.

The HAZ needs special consideration because it can easily become the weakest part of a joint. We can adjust the properties of the weld metal by changing the electrode or filler wire, but more often than not we can do little to control the properties of the HAZ while welding is in progress. Fortunately in some cases we can recover the metal properties by heat treatment after welding, but in others we have to accept the as-welded condition and decide if the joint will be satisfactory in service.

Steel

The most recognisable feature of steel is that it rusts. You only need to look at an old car to see this. It is tempting to think that because the steel components we come across in everyday life show signs of rusting all steels are the same. This would be wrong.

For a start there is the easily recognised exception in stainless steel which now plays an important role in domestic equipment. Looked after properly this does not rust. But there are other differences which are not so obvious. Steel can vary in strength. High speed drill bits are made from a different, stronger steel to that used for wood screws. The steel sheet used for car bodies can be easily pressed into shape; it is said to be ductile. On the other hand, it is difficult to change the shape of a steel spring without breaking it.

A common feature of all these steels is that they are readily fused to give a weld. So, does the welder need to know that there are different types of steel? The answer is yes, because their weldability is different. In practical terms this means that the welder must use the right electrode for strength, or be aware that there may be a special procedure to avoid cracking during welding, or that the joint may require heat treatment after welding to prepare it for service.

At this point we need to get some idea of the way in which steels differ.

Steel is an alloy. That is, it is a mixture of iron, which is a pure metal, and carbon. The mixing, or to be technically correct the alloying, is done by the steelmaker in the furnace. As a result, we cannot alter the carbon content of the plate or sheet we are using. We have to tell the supplier what properties we want from the steel so that the correct type or grade can be selected from the steel-maker's catalogue.

Only small amounts of carbon are needed to produce a significant increase in the strength. The steel sheet used for the casing of a washing machine contains as little as 0.08% carbon: in other words there are only eight parts of carbon for every ten thousand parts of iron. The plate for an oil storage tank or a small bridge contains about 0.18% carbon; in general fabrication this is one of the most common compositions and is often referred to loosely as **mild steel**. Axles are made from a 0.4% carbon steel. Further up the scale, we find wood chisels being made from a steel which contains about 0.8% carbon.

The prime effect of adding carbon is to increase the strength. For example, a 0.4% steel used for axles has about twice the tensile strength of a mild steel. The steelmaker can add other alloying elements to enhance the effect of carbon or to get other desirable properties such as better strength at high temperatures or improved resistance to rusting. The result is that there are many grades of steel. To help the purchaser, these have been classified in British Standards and other documents. The steels which feature most commonly in welded fabrications are covered by British Standard BS4360:1985 and a summary of these is given in Table 1.

Almost invariably the steel plate or pipe delivered to the customer has a higher strength than the minimum specified below for the appropriate Grade.

Table 1
Weldable steels for structural work

Grade	Yield stress Newtons/mm^2	Tensile strength Newtons/mm^2
40	230	400
43	250	430
50	340	500
55	415	550

Carbon also gives steels a unique characteristic amongst metals – they can be hardened by heat treatment. This is done by heating a steel to about 1200°C, when it looks bright orange in colour, and then plunging it into water. The operation is known as **quenching**.

The level of hardness achieved by quenching depends on two factors: the amount of carbon in the steel and the cooling rate. The higher the carbon content the greater the degree of hardening. Chisels are made from a 0.8% carbon steel because the hardness can be increased by as much as two and a half times on quenching. When the carbon content is below 0.4%, however, it is difficult to produce hardening by quenching.

The rate of cooling is also important. A steel which cools rapidly during quenching is harder than one cooled at a slower rate. Sometimes oil is used for quenching with the object of slowing the cooling rate. Why should we want to do this? Well, some steels become brittle when they are hardened. As a result they crack during quenching. A quench with a slower cooling rate can still give a significant increase in hardness, but without the risk of cracking.

HAZ cracking in welded joints

This brings us back to welding. Cooling rates in a welded joint are so fast that even in a Grade 50 plate, which only contains a low level of carbon, a hardened HAZ may be produced with the attendant risk that it may contain cracks (Fig. 5.1).

How do we avoid this in practice? The first direct action is to try to slow the cooling rate in the HAZ by heating the parent metal before welding. Preheating, as it is called, can be done in a variety of ways. The most common method in general fabrication practice is to use a propane heating torch. The metal must be heated to a distance of at least five times its thickness on either side of the joint line. It is important to apply the torch to both surfaces of the parent metal as the centre must reach the preheat temperature.

Another important point about preheating is to have the metal hot at the moment we start welding. It is no use heating the joint area and then leaving it for an hour or so before welding, by which time it has cooled. Preheating is not a pre-conditioning treatment, it must be an integral part of the welding operation to be effective.

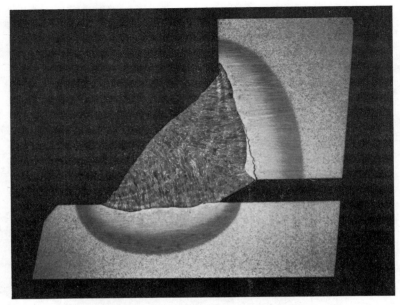

Fig. 5.1   Heat affected zone cracking in a fillet weld

How hot should the metal be? This is not an easy question to answer because it depends on so many factors, but it is usually between 75°C and 175°C. A useful source of more precise information is BS5135:1986: *Arc welding of carbon and carbon manganese steels*. This document has a series of charts which give preheat temperatures for various steels. It also lists the factors which must be taken into account. The most important of these are:

Thickness   The need for preheating increases with thickness. Thin sheets, say 3 mm and below, rarely need preheating. With most steels which are prone to cracking, pre-heating starts to get important with thicknesses of 18 mm and above.

Joint type   T-joints give faster cooling rates because there are three paths for the heat to escape compared with two in a butt joint, so we need a higher preheat temperature for a T-joint (Fig. 5.2).

Heat input   Large weld pools mean slower cooling rates in the HAZ, although there is a limit to how far we can take this. With high welding currents and slow travel speeds we can often use a lower preheat.

Steel type   Not all steels are prone to cracking. If we know the composition of the steel, BS5135 gives a formula which allows for the effect not only of carbon, but also other alloying elements which the steelmaker adds to get special properties. Often, especially in a small workshop or at home, we cannot get information about the composition. In these cases we can take it that Grade 40 and 43 steels, including the so-called mild steels, do not need pre-heating if the thickness is less than about 25 mm. On the other hand, with Grades 50 and 55, and other higher strength steels such as those used for axle shafts or tools, it is usually advisable to heat to about 175°C for safety.

Before we leave HAZ cracking in steels we must look at a less obvious but very important factor. If there is any hydrogen dis-

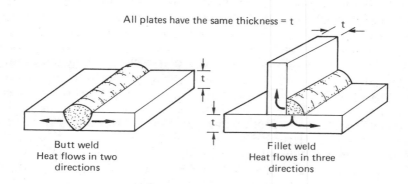

All plates have the same thickness = t

t

t

t

t

Butt weld
Heat flows in two
directions

Fillet weld
Heat flows in three
directions

Heat escapes faster from fillet weld than from
the butt weld – cooling rate is faster

Fig. 5.2   Cooling effects in butt and fillet welds

solved in the weld metal, the risk of cracking is increased enormously. Hydrogen principally comes from moisture which is decomposed in the arc. In MMA welding the moisture is introduced via the flux which may be damp. More importantly the flux can also contain water which is chemically combined with the constituents of the flux. In Chapter 9 we will be taking a closer look at the different types of flux covering used in MMA welding. For the moment we can just note that electrodes used for the welding of steels which are liable to suffer from HAZ cracking must be stored in ovens at 150°C as soon as the packet has been opened. They must be kept in the oven until they are needed for welding and even then they must be used within 20 minutes after removal. If they are exposed to the atmosphere for longer than this they need to be reheated to a much higher temperature according to the manufacturer's instructions to bring the moisture content back to a tolerable level.

From the point of view of hydrogen content, gas shielded processes are much better. The gases used for TIG and MAG welding are inherently low in moisture and, provided the equipment is in good condition, there should be little or no water in the gas which surrounds the arc. As a result, TIG and MAG offer us the prospect of very low hydrogen levels in the weld pool. This means that, especially with MAG using currents above 300A, it is possible to weld some grades of high strength steel in thicknesses up to 25 mm without the need for preheating.

Weld metal cracking
When a weld solidifies, the last part of it to change from molten to solid is the centreline. You may remember that when we were talking about distortion in Chapter 3, we said that the shrinkage set up stresses across the weld. If the centreline of the solidifying weld metal is weak, it cannot withstand these stresses and a crack is formed. In steel, there are three situations where this can happen.

The first mainly occurs with rods or bars. If the steel is to be machined to shape using a lathe or miller, or if a screw thread is to be cut on it, there is a major advantage in using a free-cutting steel. This is one where the steelmaker has added sulphur to modify the way in which chips of metal are formed during machining. Whilst the sulphur may be of great help to the machinist, it is a major handicap in welding because it leaves a film of liquid iron sulphide along the centreline of the weld. This remains molten to quite low temperatures, well below the solidification point of the steel. As a result the centreline has no strength just at the time when contraction stresses are building up across it, and a crack is formed. As a general rule, free-cutting steels should not be welded. It is better to use brazing, soldering or a mechanical method where these steels need to be joined.

The second case is where a weld is deposited which is not large enough to take the contraction stresses. This mainly happens with a root run, possibly because insufficient current is available to make a weld of adequate size or the welder is travelling fast on a poor fit-up for fear of the weld collapsing.

Finally, the weld profile can be wrong. If the depth of the weld bead is more than one and a half times the width, a crack can be formed along the centreline (Fig. 5.3). This type of cracking is only found in the welding of relatively thick plate, say 25 mm and above, with high current MAG or submerged arc processes.

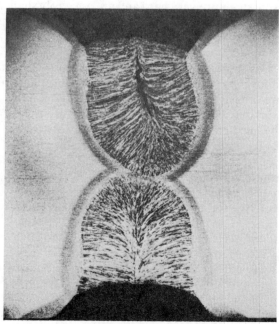

Fig. 5.3   Centre line cracking in a weld in steel

Stainless steel

There are many applications where the strength of a steel is needed but with a surface that does not rust or oxidise when it is heated and which is resistant to corrosive chemicals. Stainless steel is now commonplace in the home. It is used for sinks, cooking utensils and washing machines. In industry, stainless steels are essential in chemical and food processing plants.

The ability to resist corrosive attack comes from the addition of chromium to the steel during the steelmaking operation. As with the steels we discussed in the preceding sections, there is more than one type of stainless steel and the chromium content varies between 12% and 25% according to the application.

There are two main types of stainless steel – **martensitic** and **austenitic**. The names refer to the metallurgical structure which would be seen under a microscope. To a large extent the properties are determined by this structure.

Martensitic steels are very hard and are not easily shaped or bent without fracturing. They contain about 12% or 13% chromium and are the steels traditionally used for cutlery, although they are often replaced in modern knives and forks by austenitic steels. Another familiar use is in the manufacture of golf clubs. The martensitic steels used for these products are high in carbon and are not suited to fusion welding as the welds crack badly. A low carbon, weldable grade is available and offers properties which are right for certain types of chemical plant. Whilst it is relatively easy to fuse the joint and control the weld pool, special procedures are needed to avoid cracking, and technical knowledge is needed in the selection of the most appropriate electrode. The most readily welded type of martensitic steel is coded as Grade 410. In the workshop it can be distinguished from other stainless steels by the fact that it is strongly magnetic.

Austenitic steels are usually non-magnetic, although a few grades are slightly attracted by a magnet. A principal feature of austenitic stainless steels is that they are readily shaped by bending or pressing. They contain 18% to 25% chromium and 8% to 12% nickel along with other alloying elements such as molybdenum. Often they are called 18/8 (eighteen-eight) steels although strictly this describes just one grade. The austenitic steels are coded using a number

Table 2
Typical austenitic stainless steels

Grade	Chromium %	Nickel %	Others
304L	18.5	10.0	
309L	22.0	12.0	
316L	17.0	12.0	Molybdenum
321	18.0	9.0	Titanium
347	19.0	10.0	Niobium

beginning with a 3; a list of the more important weldable grades is given in Table 2.

From the point of view of the welding operation, three factors must be taken into account.

Firstly, the surface of the joint must be thoroughly cleaned. Any brushing must be done with a stainless steel wire brush. If an ordinary carbon steel brush is used, the surface becomes contaminated with iron and some of its corrosion resistance is lost.

Secondly, large weld runs have a tendency to crack. This can be offset by travelling fast or reducing the current to give small individual weld beads. Pre-heating should not be used.

Thirdly, slow cooling in the HAZ can lead to a loss of corrosion resistance in this region of the joint and rapid attack in service. The technical name for this is **intergranular corrosion**, but it is more commonly known as **weld decay**. The stainless steels listed in Table 2 do not suffer from this problem provided the heat input from welding is not excessive. They should not be preheated and the joint should be cooled quickly after welding. Steels not listed may suffer from intergranular corrosion in the HAZ and for these other methods of jointing should be considered.

TIG (electrode negative) and MMA welding are the most usual processes for stainless steel. Matching filler wires and electrodes are readily available. Successful results can also be obtained with MAG welding using an argon-1% oxygen shielding gas. Although oxy-acetylene welding is possible, using a flux, the results are not as satisfactory as those obtained with TIG or MMA.

Austenitic stainless steels are readily spot welded. They have a higher electrical resistance than mild steel so it is possible to use a lower current setting. A higher pressure on the electrodes is needed, however, which means that with thicker sheets the arms of the machine must be more rigid. If not, there is a tendency for the electrodes to move sideways thus coming out of line and reducing the pressure on the sheet which in turn leads to an unsound weld.

Aluminium alloys

Aluminium is most notable as a lightweight metal which has a bright surface. In everyday life we find it being used for soft drink cans, cooking utensils, car trim and window frames. For many years it has been the principal metal in the construction of aircraft. It has good resistance to corrosion and is suitable for use in storage tanks and vessels; draught beer is delivered to public houses in aluminium barrels or kegs.

Once again we are dealing not with one metal but a number of alloys, many of which have poor weldability. We are unlikely to meet a number of the higher strength alloys outside specialised industries such as aerospace so we can concentrate on the more commonly available grades.

Pure aluminium, as its name implies, is unalloyed. It is soft and does not have very high strength. On the other hand, it can be readily shaped by pressing and when polished gives a highly reflective surface. Some increase in strength can be obtained in the manufacture of aluminium sheet by rolling it cold to reduce the thickness. This hardens the metal and the sheet is said to be quarter-hard, half-hard or hard according to the amount of rolling which has taken place. The hardness is quickly lost when the aluminium is heated to about 150°C, so if we weld, say, a half-hard sheet the HAZ will be softened by the heating effect of the weld and will revert to the lower strength of soft aluminium. Unfortunately, the hardness cannot be recovered and we must accept that the joint will be weaker than the parent metal.

A useful range of alloys is produced by adding magnesium to aluminium. These alloys are ideal for the fabrication of storage tanks and, because they have good resistance to seawater corrosion, they are used for the superstructure of ships. Like pure aluminium they can be hardened in manufacture to give higher strength and so softening occurs in the HAZ of a welded joint.

Both pure aluminium and the aluminium-magnesium alloys are weldable although the weld pool is not easy to control. The melting point of aluminium is low (660°C) and the weld metal quickly becomes fluid. When welding sheet, travel speeds must be fast to avoid the risk of the pool collapsing through the root.

The surface of a piece of aluminium is covered with a continuous skin of oxide which gives the metal its good corrosion resistance. This oxide skin has a high melting point and must be removed by the welding process as it will act as a sack holding the molten aluminium and preventing the formation of a weld pool.

The best results are obtained with gas shielded processes, i.e. TIG (a.c.) and MIG. Both of these systems disperse the oxide film, thus allowing good fusion, and the gas shield prevents further oxidation. Pure argon must be used and the moisture content must be low to minimise the risk of porosity. Note that for TIG welding of aluminium, alternating current is essential. Direct current does not disperse the oxide with TIG, but it does work with MIG welding.

Whilst it is possible to produce acceptable welds with the oxy-acetylene process, a flux is needed to dissolve the oxide. This causes corrosion of the joint if it is not completely removed after welding. Similarly MMA electrodes use a flux which is highly corrosive and gives off fumes during welding – these pose a health hazard if ventilation is poor. In general, it is better to use TIG or MIG for aluminium.

Filler metals for welding aluminium alloys are available as cut lengths, 1 metre long, for TIG welding, and wound onto spools for MIG welding; larger spools contain 4.5kg (10lb) whilst small spools containing ½kg (1lb) are supplied for use on lightweight machines. The wires are given a code number for identification. In the UK the designation is covered by British Standard BS2901 (see Appendix 6). For welding pure aluminium a 1080A or 1050B filler is used. In general it is good practice to match the filler wires to the individual compositions of the aluminium-magnesium alloys, but for economy one filler – 5056A – may be used for the whole range.

If we want higher strength from an aluminium alloy, we must turn to heat treatment. The most widely known heat-treatable alloy is undoubtedly Dural. In fact, Dural or Duralumin is a trade name for a particular alloy of aluminium and copper. Aluminium-copper welds crack along the centreline if they are welded with matching filler. Sound welds can be obtained with an aluminium-10% silicon filler (4047) but this has very low strength and cannot be heat treated.

Another heat-treatable alloy, which is widely used for window frames and similar extrusions, is aluminium-magnesium-silicon. It also cracks along the centreline of the weld if welded with an aluminium-magnesium-silicon filler. To avoid cracking an aluminium-5% silicon filler (4043) must be used. This has a higher strength than 4047 filler but is still well below that of the parent metal.

The only alloy which can recover most of its HAZ hardness and joint strength after welding is aluminium-zinc-magnesium. There is an added advantage in that it is not necessary to heat treat, as the alloy hardens by itself over a period of about fourteen days. This is a phenomenon known as natural ageing and it takes place at normal air temperatures. So, provided we are not in a hurry to put the joint into service, the component can be left on the shop floor while it hardens. Special filler wires are available from stockists for welding aluminium-zinc-magnesium alloys.

Copper alloys

Pure copper

From the point of view of welding, perhaps the most important feature of copper is its high thermal conductivity. This may be highly desirable in a copper-bottomed kettle where we want the heat to be conducted quickly from the gas flame to the water. But it is a major handicap when we are trying to weld copper with the oxy-acetylene process. It is most likely that the heat will be conducted away from the joint before the faces of the joint preparation have been fused.

The chances of success are greater with arc welding, but we need to use higher currents on copper than would be normal for welding the same thickness of steel, to offset the rate of heat loss due to the high thermal conductivity.

TIG welding is suitable for material up to 3 mm thick. Argon is usually used, but better results are obtained with helium which gives a 'hotter' arc as the arc voltage is higher.

Material over 3 mm thick needs pre-heating if TIG is used and it is preferable to switch to MIG with argon or argon-helium shielding. Even with MIG it is common practice to preheat joints in material thicker than 12 mm. Note that preheating in this case is not aimed at preventing cracking as with steels, but simply to assist in fusing the faces of the joint. MIG welding of copper calls for considerable skill as the welder must ensure that the parent metal is fused before it is covered by the molten metal from the electrode. If this is not done, there is no bonding to the parent metal and a wedge of weld metal can be lifted from the joint. With the high currents needed for welding copper it is common practice to use water-cooled nozzles on MIG guns.

Porosity forms very readily in welds in copper. Some of this arises from moisture on the joint surfaces or in the shielding gas. It is unusual for gas in the cylinder to be moist, and where the source of the porosity is identified as the gas around the arc, it is usually due to a leak in the water-cooled nozzle or in the gas line. Porosity can also arise from chemical reactions in the weld pool; these are suppressed by the use of filler wires which contain deoxidants, i.e. alloying elements which remove oxygen from the molten metal.

Aluminium bronze

Alloying copper with about 10% of its weight in aluminium produces a metal which has a bright gold-coloured surface and has good corrosion resistance. The aluminium addition reduces the thermal conductivity of the metal and it is easier to get fusion of the joint faces. Preheating is not necessary; in fact it can be harmful since slow cooling rates in the joint can lead to cracking.

TIG and MIG welding are the preferred processes. With TIG it is necessary to use a.c. to disperse the oxide film, as would be done with aluminium and its alloys.

Brass

One of the most familiar alloys of copper is brass. It contains between 30% and 40% zinc and was widely used in engineering earlier this century. It is now less common and tends to be found more in decorative work.

Brass can be readily welded in as much as it can be fused to give a controllable weld pool. The heat of welding, however, vaporises the zinc which is deposited as a white powder (zinc oxide) on the joint surfaces. Dezincification is difficult to control in both arc and oxy-acetylene welding and it is generally better to use a non-fusion joining technique such as silver soldering.

Fume hazards
Both copper and brass give off fumes during welding which can be harmful, and good ventilation is essential. The presence of copper oxide fume in the atmosphere gives a taste in the mouth similar to sucking a twopenny piece. It must be stressed that the absence of such a sensation does not mean that there is no copper oxide fume present. Inhalation of either copper oxide or zinc oxide produces symptoms similar to those of influenza – the condition is known as copper or zinc fever.

Cast and wrought irons

In the earlier part of this chapter we saw that steel was an alloy of iron and carbon. The largest content of carbon we looked at was 0.8%. If larger amounts of carbon are added, the iron becomes harder and brittle. At the same time, however, it also becomes more fluid in the molten state and is ideally suited to casting.

Cast iron contains from 2.5% to 4.0% carbon together with other alloying elements such as silicon, manganese and phosphorus. It is difficult to weld and calls for special techniques to avoid cracking. Cast iron is normally only welded as a repair when a casting has been fractured and the essential elements of typical procedures are described in Chapter 12.

Wrought iron should not be confused with cast iron. It is low in carbon – about 0.05% – and is very ductile, which is why it was popular in the blacksmith's forge. Nowadays, most of the metal called wrought iron used in gates and the like is really low carbon steel. Wrought iron is expensive to produce and is found only in antiques. Traditionally it was welded by hammering a scarf or lap joint with the metal heated to about 1000°C (a bright red heat). Although it is possible to make a fusion weld, the pool tends to be pasty – i.e. lacking in fluidity – due to the amount of slag in the wrought iron which has melted into the pool. If wrought iron needs to be joined, say for a repair, a technique such as braze welding is preferred (see page 146).

PART TWO
Welding Practices

6

Safety in Arc Welding

Used properly, welding is a safe process and not many people suffer serious injury using it. When accidents do occur they result from carelessness or ignorance of the rules of good practice. Some hazards are readily identified. The effect on the eyes of the bright light given off by the arc is only too obvious. Other hazards are less easily identified but nonetheless exist. In this chapter we will examine some of the potential hazards and spell out the basic rules of safe practice.

We can start by listing the areas of greatest risk (Fig. 6.1).

1   Ultraviolet radiation
2   Fire
3   Electric shock
4   Fumes
5   Gas cylinders

Ultraviolet radiation

The arc emits a high level of white light. This is capable of causing extreme discomfort to the eye, but its effect can be readily reduced by viewing the arc through a darkened screen. Quite apart from the safety aspect, the screen is also needed to get a good view of the weld pool and joint line. Trying to view the arc without the screen would be like looking at the undipped headlights of an oncoming car.

In addition to the visible light, the arc gives off ultraviolet rays (UV). These are the same as the rays which come from the sun and which produce a tanning effect on the skin. In welding the level of

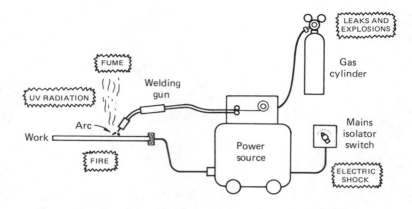

Fig. 6.1   Principal safety hazards in arc welding

UV radiation is appreciably higher than we receive from the sun. It can very quickly cause burning of the skin especially when welding at currents above 100A. The problem is worse with gas shielded processes like TIG and MIG than with MMA welding. With MMA, the flux tends to reduce the intensity of the rays. In submerged arc welding the arc is not exposed as it operates beneath the flux layer and the problem does not arise.

The welder should be protected by wearing an overall which covers the arms and the area under the chin. It is also advisable to wear gloves, especially with MIG/MAG welding. These should be gauntlets with the sleeves of the overall tucked into the top so that the wrists are not inadvertently exposed to the arc.

If the welding arc is viewed directly, the UV burns the tissue of the eyeball leading to a condition known as **arc eye**. The effects may not be immediately obvious but can become extremely painful. Usually some hours transpire before the symptoms are noticed. Arc eye is characterised by a burning sensation in the eye and feeling as if there is sand under the eyelids. Although arc eye can be frightening when first experienced and may make it difficult for the sufferer to see clearly, it is transitory and self-healing. The pain can be eased by eyedrops but these are more effective if they are applied immediately after any accidental exposure to UV; a suitable preparation can be supplied by a chemist. If the pain persists for more than twenty-four hours, medical advice must be sought.

Eye protection is provided by a filter fitted to the helmet or face shield (Fig. 6.2). This is usually combined with the darkened glass which reduces the level of illumination. The filter is used with a piece of plain glass on the side facing the arc which protects it against damage by spatter or fume. The protective glass is relatively cheap and can be replaced at regular intervals. The helmet or face shield also helps to protect the welder's skin against burning. A hand-held shield is very commonly used in arc welding and can give adequate protection. A helmet is to be preferred, however, as it leaves both hands free.

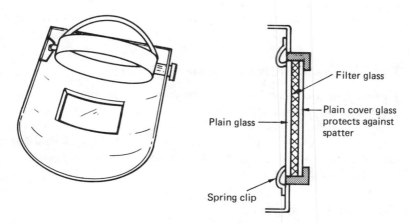

Fig. 6.2   Helmet and filter glass

Filter glasses are graded according to the amount of light they allow through. In the British Standard system each filter is given a grade number ranging from four to fourteen; a high number indicates that the filter is darker and therefore absorbs more light. The amount of light from the arc depends on the current and the process being used to make the weld. So, the recommended grade number can be related to the current level. For arc welding the most common grades are nine to thirteen (see Table 3).

Very often the person at greatest risk of getting arc eye is not the welder but the onlooker. Both the visible and UV radiations from

Table 3
Recommended filters for arc welding

BS 679 Shade	Current Range – Amps		
	TIG	MIG/MAG	MMA
9EW	15 to 75		up to 100
10EW	75 to 100	up to 200	100 to 300
11EW	100 to 200	up to 200	100 to 300
12EW	200 to 250	over 200	over 300
13EW	250 to 300	over 200	over 300

the arc are readily reflected from polished surfaces such as a piece of brightly finished metal or a mirror or a white wall. These reflections can cause arc eye in anyone who happens to glance at the reflecting surfaces.

Eye protection with oxy-acetylene welding

Although the oxy-acetylene flame does not give off ultraviolet rays, the welder's eyes must still be protected to prevent damage by heat and bright light. Goggles are adequate provided they are fitted with suitable lens. A Grade 4GW is recommended for light work whilst a Grade 5GW should be used with the larger flames needed for welding plate material.

Burns and fire hazards

It goes without saying that a lot of heat is generated by the welding arc. Even so, it is often forgotten that it takes some time for the workpiece to cool down and frequently burns result from picking up a hot component after welding. Another source of burns is touching the hot tip of an electrode, during changing, in MMA welding.

The arc also emits infra-red rays. The mask protects the welder's face from these rays, but they can cause scorching of clothing. Protective clothing should be of the right texture and fire retardant. Advice should always be sought from the manufacturers of industrial protective clothing.

Another hazard associated with the heat from welding is fire. Often small droplets of molten metal – spatter – are ejected from the weld pool. If these fall onto combustible material they can start a fire. Hot slag chipped from a weld is a similar fire hazard.

Perhaps the most serious risk is run when welding near flammable liquids such as petrol. Where a vessel which has contained a flammable liquid is to be welded, probably as part of a repair procedure, all traces of it must first be removed. The most common situation of this type is welding near a petrol tank when repairing a car.

Flammable liquids are sometimes used in the workshop for cleaning or degreasing purposes. They constitute a major hazard and when welding is involved, non-flammable degreasers should be used.

A fire extinguisher and a bucket of sand should always be on hand when welding is taking place.

Electrical hazards

As with any electrical appliance, the user must always be on guard against electric shock. With welding equipment the first source of danger lies in the mains lead which is connected to the input side of the power supply unit. The 13A plug and plastic covered cable fitted to small units are prone to damage by burning or by allowing pieces of metal with sharp edges to fall on them. The wire which is exposed by such damage is carrying 240 volts (V) and would electrocute anyone touching it. Industrial units often operate with an input of 380 to 440V and should be connected to the mains socket with a correctly protected plug. Any wiring of the input or primary side of an industrial power source should only be undertaken by a qualified electrician.

The power source is designed so that the secondary – i.e. the welding – side is isolated from the mains, thus protecting the welder (Fig. 6.3). The voltages used on the secondary side during welding are relatively low and do not normally give rise to the risk of shock. With MMA and TIG welding, however, there is a relatively high voltage on the electrode before the arc is struck and the current flows. This is called the open circuit voltage (OCV). With conventional equipment the OCV ranges from 60 to 100V, and in damp conditions this is sufficiently high to give a shock. Some people are more at risk than others from these voltages and it is always good

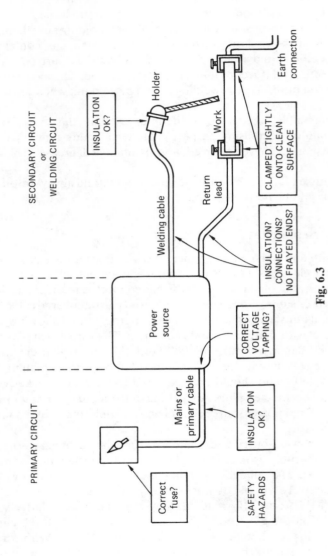

Fig. 6.3

practice to avoid touching the bare electrode before striking the arc if the power is switched on. With many MMA sets, there is no contactor or switch in the welding circuit so the electrode is live as long as the mains is switched on – a glove should be worn when changing the electrode.

Another possible source of high voltage is the use of hand tools by a person other than the welder working on the same component. Someone may be grinding elsewhere on the fabrication and whilst they will be protected against the possible breakdown of the hand-held grinding tool this does not prevent the mains voltage being coupled to the work and therefore to the welder operating the arc. To reduce these risks, the workpiece should be separately earthed (Fig. 6.4). Frequently the welding return lead (i.e. the cable that goes from the workpiece to the power source to carry the welding current) is called an earth. This is incorrect. An earth lead is a separate cable clipped to the workpiece which goes back to the mains earth or to some metal frame which is firmly trenched into the ground. Safe practice recommendations for the avoidance of electrical accidents during welding are given in a document prepared and issued by the Health and Safety Executive.

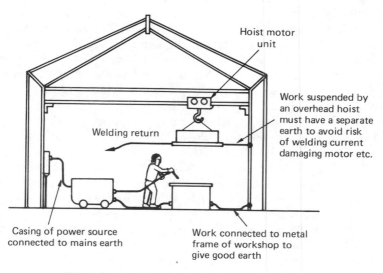

Fig. 6.4 Earthing the work during arc welding

Fume

In the heat of the arc, some metal and flux is vaporised to form visible fume which rises around the welder's face. Some of this fume is relatively harmless and acts only as an irritant if the welder inhales it. Other components of the fume can be dangerous to health. Medical research conducted in centres around the world has been able to identify chemical compounds which can lead to health problems such as deterioration of the lungs, respiratory difficulties and cancer. In many cases the risk which arises from being exposed to these chemicals is related to the length of time the person is exposed to them. We can get a guide to the toxicity of the various chemicals in welding fume by reference to the list of Occupational Exposure Limits (OEL) which is published by the Health and Safety Executive. These indicate the maximum concentration that the welder can be exposed to on the basis of a normal working shift. They are not statutory limits, but they do provide the basis for the assessment of whether or not an atmosphere is acceptable for working.

Frequently the main fume hazard comes not from the electrode and its covering but from coatings on the workpiece. One such coating is cadmium which is plated onto the steel to produce a corrosion resistant surface. Cadmium oxide is formed in the heat of the arc and is very toxic – cadmium-plated objects should not be welded. Similarly, galvanised materials generate an obnoxious fume containing zinc oxide. Whilst this is less toxic than cadmium oxide it can cause zinc fever which has symptoms similar to influenza.

The risks from fume must be kept in perspective, however, and they can be considerably reduced by the use of safe working practices ensuring good ventilation.

The first point to check is the position of the welder's head (Fig. 6.5). By adjusting the position of the work, it is often possible to avoid the need for the welder to be in line with the fume plume as it rises from the work.

Undoubtedly the most satisfactory method of fume protection from the welder's point of view is to use a helmet which provides a continuous supply of fresh air to the breathing zone. These are expensive, they tend to be cumbersome and they do not obviate the

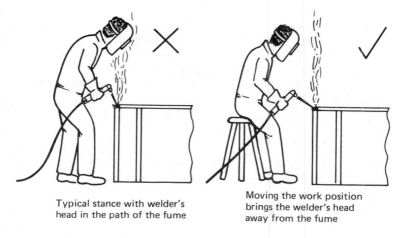

Typical stance with welder's head in the path of the fume

Moving the work position brings the welder's head away from the fume

Fig. 6.5 Adjusting working posture to minimise exposure to fume

need to ventilate the remainder of the shop to protect other workers in the area.

A successful alternative to this helmet is to remove the welding fume close to the arc (Fig. 6.6). This can be done by an extraction system which operates rather like a vacuum cleaner sucking the air away from the welding zone. A fan shaped nozzle is attached to the hose leading to the extractor so that the length of the joint being welded can be covered. The fume laden air can be filtered before being discharged back into the workshop. Alternatively, the outlet from the extraction fan can be vented outside the workshop itself. This is the preferred practice, but it does lead to heat losses from the workshop.

In addition to visible fume the arc generates gases. The two most important of these from the health point of view are ozone and oxides of nitrogen. Contrary to popular belief, ozone is not beneficial to health, at least in the concentrations that exist around the welding arc. Breathing ozone into the lungs leads to the formation of pockets of water under the lung tissue which bring about breathing difficulties. This condition can be treated but clearly it is better to remove the ozone before it is inhaled by the welder. Ozone

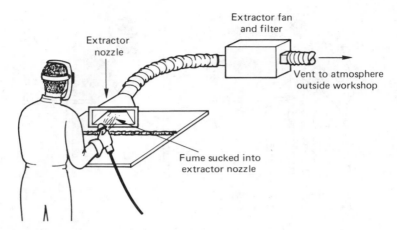

Fig. 6.6   Using local ventilation to remove fume from the welder's
breathing zone

decomposes readily in contact with fabric and is therefore removed
by the extractor.

Nitrogen oxides, on the other hand, are not removed by the
filtering system. If inhaled in significant amounts, these gases are
absorbed into the blood stream causing cyanosis. Normally the
amount of nitrogen oxides produced by arc welding is not large, but
if the output from the extraction system is vented into a part of the
workshop where the concentration could build up, workers in that
area could be affected. In these circumstances it is much better to
vent to the outside.

With MAG welding, using carbon dioxide as a shielding gas,
there is a slight risk that carbon monoxide concentrations may be
built up if the arc is not operating correctly. Once again this problem
can be solved by the use of an extraction fan but, as with oxides of
nitrogen, the effluent must be vented into the open.

Wherever possible welding in confined spaces should be avoided
and a reasonably large workshop is to be recommended. There are
times when it is necessary to weld inside a tank or an enclosed space.
In these situations good ventilation is a must, but it is not sufficient

just to extract the polluted air; fresh air must be supplied to replace it (Fig. 6.7).

If the welding is being done with the MIG/MAG process the shielding gas, argon or carbon dioxide, is heavier than air and settles at the bottom of the tank. With prolonged periods of welding the air may be displaced from the tank leaving the welder working in an atmosphere of argon or carbon dioxide. The result is asphyxiation. The shielding gas must be extracted from the bottom of the tank and replaced by fresh air introduced at a level above the welder's head.

A welder should never work alone inside a tank. There must always be someone on watch outside and a rope should be attached to the welder so that a rapid rescue can be effected.

Working with gas cylinders

The shielding gas for TIG and MIG/MAG welding is supplied in cylinders under pressure. With argon and argon-carbon dioxide mixtures, the pressure is around 140 bar (2000 psi). Carbon dioxide cylinders tend to work at a lower pressure of about 11 bar (150 psi). The cylinders are fitted with regulators which reduce the pressure to

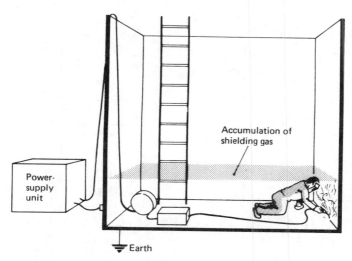

Fig. 6.7   Build-up of shielding gas at bottom of enclosed space. Warning: always have a person standing by when welding in an enclosed space.

that required for welding and maintain it at a constant level. Normally this pressure will be around 2 bar (30 psi).

A cylinder used for welding must always be firmly secured to prevent it falling over (Fig. 6.8). If the cylinder does fall, breaking the regulator, it becomes jet propelled and can cause considerable damage.

Regulators must be maintained in good condition and should not be hammered during removal from the cylinder. Any leaks which occur must not be repaired by an amateur. The damaged unit must be returned to the supplier for repair and testing. Grease or oil must never be used on a regulator which has a sticking control knob, a jammed thread or a leaky connection – grease in contact with pure oxygen causes an explosion.

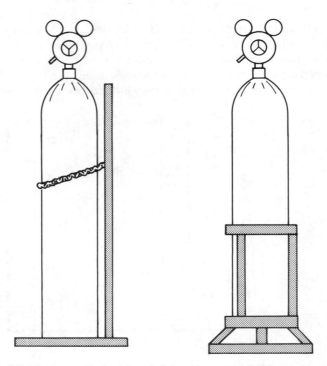

Fig. 6.8　Secure cylinders by chaining to a stable object or by using a suitable stand

Leaks in gas lines must never be sealed with plumber's paste or similar compounds. If a connector is leaking it is probably because the seating is damaged and it must be replaced. Similarly the fixing of the hose to the connector should be made with the correct clamping device, not with odd bits of wire.

Cylinders should always be kept upright in a cool place and should be well away from the welding operation to avoid the risk of touching them accidentally with the electrode.

Golden rules for safe working with welding

1 Always use protective clothing which is fire retardant.
2 Wear protective footwear.
3 Use the correct grade of filter in a headshield and remember to change the grade to suit the level of current. Never look at the arc with the naked eye.
4 Avoid welding in wet conditions.
5 Always earth the workpiece.
6 Use local extraction positioned near the arc to remove welding fume. Vent the output from the extractor to open atmosphere.
7 Ensure good general ventilation for the workshop.
8 Provide fresh air in addition to extraction when working in confined spaces.
9 Remove all combustible material from the area before starting to weld.
10 Store gas cylinders safely in the upright position.

7

Learning to Weld

You cannot learn to weld by reading a book.

The key to successful welding is control of the weld pool. This means that the welder must be able not only to fuse the edges of the workpieces and so create a weld pool, but also to regulate the movement of the molten metal so that it does not run ahead of the arc, which would lead to lack of fusion, or run out of the joint.

Mastering the techniques of both arc and gas welding requires much practice to achieve the hand-to-eye co-ordination which is essential for success. The best way to learn is under the supervision of a skilled instructor either on a company training scheme or in a commercial, college or public training school. The printed word can, however, give guidelines and offer hints and tips which help you out of your difficulties. Videos also provide a valuable aid to learning (see Appendix 2).

In this chapter we will look at some of the essential principles of welding practice and describe six exercises which will help you acquire the basic skills needed to control the weld pool. The exercises are based on welding steel because this is the most common requirement. It is also easier and cheaper to buy offcuts of steel sheet and plate. The skills acquired on steel can be transferred to other metals once you have become proficient in welding.

Before you start welding

Getting things right is usually easier if you work to a set routine. This is very true of welding. Once welding has begun, you want to continue uninterrupted until the joint is completed, stopping only to do essential tasks such as changing electrodes. It is a good idea to establish a set pattern of checks before you start to weld. This can be worked out to suit your own requirements but here is a typical check-list to give you some ideas:

1   Do not have any combustible materials in the area where you are welding.

2   Remove anything which might obstruct your movements. Remember that you cannot see much through the screen apart from the arc and the weld pool.

3   Check that the ventilation system is working and that all safety precautions have been taken. For example, make sure that the fire extinguisher is close to hand.

4   Place a metal bin near the workbench to take hot material such as the stub ends of MMA electrodes or slag which has been removed from the weld.

5   Check that mains and cable connections are in good order.

6   Check the content of the gas cylinders to see if there is sufficient gas left to complete the weld. This can be read from the gauges on the regulators but the small cylinders supplied with portable sets rarely have gauges and the only answer is to check the weight.

7   Ensure that there is an adequate supply of electrodes or filler metal rods to hand.

8   Check the operation of the drive motor in MIG/MAG welding.

9   Find a comfortable position. Avoid having to overstretch to reach the joint. With oxy-acetylene welding, if possible sit so that you can support your arms on the bench. You can control your hand movements better if you are relaxed.

10   Warn any onlookers before you strike the arc so that they are not exposed to the risk of arc eye.

Starting the weld

Starting the weld is often the most difficult hurdle for the learner. In arc welding, there are two distinct aspects to be mastered – striking the arc and establishing the correct size of weld pool. With oxy-acetylene welding, the first task is to get the correct flame and then attention can be given to forming the pool.

Practise on a piece of 6 mm thick scrap steel. Start the weld in the way described below for the process you are using. As soon as the surface of the steel melts, use a small circular motion of the electrode or the torch to make a weld pool about 20 mm in diameter (roughly the size of a penny). Then stop welding and try again at another point. Keep practising until you feel confident. It is a good idea to let the plate cool between each attempt.

MMA welding

To strike the arc in MMA welding, hold the electrode at an angle of about 70° to the horizontal and with the tip 10 mm above the surface (Fig. 7.1). Keep it in this position while you cover your face with your headshield and then move the electrode quickly with a pendulum motion so that the tip scratches the surface of the steel. As soon as you see a spark, withdraw the electrode so that the arc gap is about twice the diameter of the core wire. Watch the surface of the steel for signs of melting. When these are evident, shorten the arc length slightly and move the tip of the electrode in a small circular motion to make the weld pool.

Break the arc by pulling the electrode away from the workpiece. Chip the slag from the weld and check that the surface is smooth and fused into the steel at the edge.

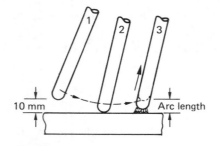

1   Hold electrode at an angle of 70° to the plate surface

2   Scratch the tip along the surface of work

3   As soon as the arc starts open gap to 2 × diameter of core wire (= arc length)

Fig. 7.1 Scratch starting the arc

MIG/MAG welding

Striking the arc with MIG/MAG is much easier than with MMA welding. Simply position the tip of the wire electrode on the metal surface at the beginning of the weld, press the trigger and the arc starts automatically (Fig. 7.2). Take care not to react to the arc by pulling the gun away from the sheet. Hold the gun steady until a weld pool has been formed.

Warning: *Before you start welding, check if the electrode wire is live, i.e. carrying the open circuit voltage. If it is, the arc will start as soon as the wire touches the surface of the steel. Refer to your instruction manual.*

Most MIG/MAG sets have a contactor built into them which isolates the wire from the power source until the trigger is pressed to start the wire feed motor. But a number of low cost sets do not incorporate this feature. If this is the case with the set you are using, start the welding operation by holding the tip of the electrode 5 mm above the surface of the workpiece. Position your headshield and press the trigger when you are ready.

During welding, the nozzle should be 20 mm from the surface of the workpiece. With this spacing, the **stick-out** – the length of wire protruding from the contact tip – is 10 to 12 mm. If the stick-out is longer than 12 mm the penetrating power of the arc is reduced. Moving the nozzle closer to the work surface brings the danger that

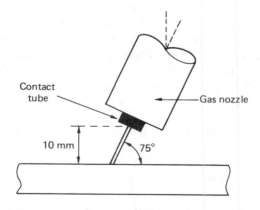

Fig. 7.2   Starting MIG/MAG welding

the arc will melt the contact tip and fuse it to the electrode – a **burn-back**. The instruction manual for your welding set should tell you how to clear a burn-back.

As soon as the arc has been established, adjust the nozzle-to-plate distance to 20 mm and move the electrode tip in a small circle to give a 20 mm diameter weld pool.

Break the arc by releasing the trigger and withdrawing the gun to 30 mm from the work. Keep it at this distance so that the weld metal is protected by the shielding gas until the pool has solidified.

The mistake most frequently made by the novice is to react to the striking of the arc by pulling the gun away from the work. This reduces the effectiveness of the gas shield and could cause porosity in the weld. More importantly, this reaction brings with it the risk of lack of penetration.

Oxy-acetylene welding

The oxy-acetylene flame has a well defined structure which can be readily seen when it is viewed through goggles fitted with a suitable green filter lens. There is a small white inner cone at the tip of the nozzle which is surrounded by a blue outer flame (Fig. 7.3).

The shape and size of the inner cone is determined by the ratio of acetylene to oxygen. If there is too much acetylene the outer flame is whiter and the boundary of the inner cone is indistinct – a **reducing flame** which gives poor heat transfer and may deposit black soot on the weld. Too much oxygen makes the inner cone small and sharply defined while the outer flame is almost invisible when viewed through green goggles – an **oxidising flame** which causes eruptions in the weld pool due to chemical reactions between the excess oxygen and the molten steel. The correct balance for welding is achieved when the flame is **neutral**, i.e. there is no excess of either acetylene or oxygen.

The flame must be adjusted to neutral before starting to weld:

1   Adjust the supply pressures for the acetylene and oxygen using the regulators fitted to the cylinders. Follow the manufacturer's instructions.
2   Open the acetylene valve and ignite the gas. It burns with a sooty yellow flame.

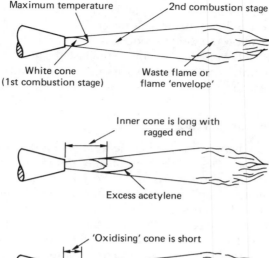

Maximum temperature

2nd combustion stage

White cone
(1st combustion stage)

Waste flame or
flame 'envelope'

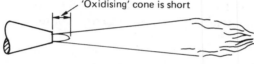

Inner cone is long with
ragged end

Excess acetylene

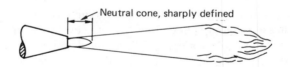

'Oxidising' cone is short

Neutral cone, sharply defined

Fig. 7.3   The oxy-acetylene flame

3   Gradually open the oxygen valve. The inner cone starts to take
on a more clearly defined shape.
4   The correct setting is when the inner cone just loses its feathery
edge and the outline becomes sharp.

The hottest part of the flame is at the tip of the inner cone so when
welding this must be just above the weld pool surface to get
maximum heating effect. To start a weld, hold the torch so that the
nozzle is at right angles to the plate surface, with the tip of the inner
cone just touching the steel. As soon as a bright spot of molten metal
appears in the centre of the heated metal move the flame in a small

circle to enlarge the pool, keeping the tip of the inner cone just above its surface. When the weld is the correct size, simply remove the torch and allow the weld to cool.

At the end of the practice session, extinguish the flame by closing the acetylene valve first, wait for two or three seconds and then close the oxygen valve.

Getting the correct angle

An important factor in controlling the weld pool is the direction of the arc or flame. This influences not only the movement of the molten metal but also the fusion of the joint faces. Solid metal cannot be melted simply by contact with molten weld metal. The joint faces must be exposed to the direct heat of the arc or flame before the weld metal can be allowed to flow over them. Control of both fusion and the movement of the weld pool is most readily achieved if the relationship of the electrode or torch is as shown in Fig. 7.4.

Basic exercises

The following six exercises are designed to give you practice in the basic skills of welding. They allow you to develop your ability to control the weld pool by starting with simple deposition of runs onto plate in the flat position and ending with welding a T-joint in the vertical position. In this way you get experience of weld pool behaviour in the main welding positions. When you have finished the sequence and have practised the skills you have acquired you can tackle overhead welding, but this is best done under the guidance of an instructor.

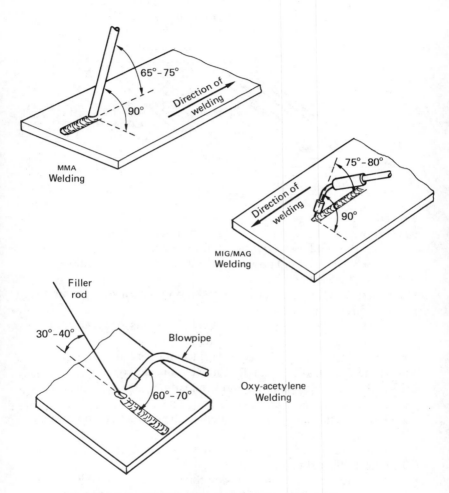

Fig. 7.4 Standard electrode and blowpipe angles

Exercise 1

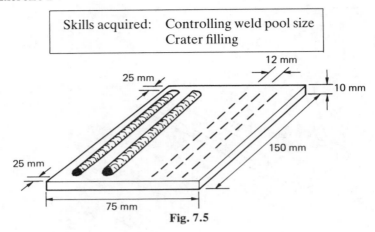

Skills acquired: Controlling weld pool size
                    Crater filling

Fig. 7.5

Procedure:
1 Draw chalk lines parallel to the long edge, 12 mm apart.
2 Start the weld pool about 25 mm from one short edge.
3 As soon as the weld pool is established, move the arc along the chalk line. Remember:
   • In MAG welding, the electrode points *forwards*, i.e. in the direction of welding.
   • In MMA welding, the electrode points *backwards*, i.e. towards the completed weld.
4 Ensure that the arc melts the surface of the plate.
5 If the weld pool gets smaller, move more slowly.
6 If the weld pool is large and the leading edge looks as if it is rolling along the plate surface, move faster.
7 Pay particular attention to keeping the correct angle between the electrode and the plate.
8 Break the arc 25 mm from the end of the plate.
9 Check the weld appearance:
   • Uneven ripple markings on the surface of the weld and/or variation in width means that the travel speed was not uniform.
   • Elongated ripples result from a fast weld speed.
   • A peaky, bulbous shaped weld run indicates that the current or voltage (arc length) was too low.

10 Deposit a second run. At the end of the run do not switch off the current immediately but pause, increase the arc length, and use a small rotary action to fill the crater.

11 Deposit further runs until the plate is covered with beads 12 mm apart. Save for the next exercise.

Exercise 2

> Skills acquired: Achieving fusion between weld runs
> Controlling weld pool size by weaving
> Stopping and starting a weld run

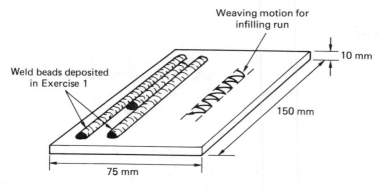

Fig. 7.6

Procedure:

1 Use the test sample from Exercise 1. Thoroughly wire brush the surface to remove all oxides and slag.

2 Start the weld pool between two weld beads. Use a circular motion of the arc to make the weld pool width equal to the distance between the weld beads.

3 Ensure that the edges of the previous weld beads are fused.

4 Move forward, at the same time using a side to side motion of the arc (*weaving*). Pause briefly (*dwell*) at each edge to ensure fusion into the previous weld and to build up the thickness of the weld.

5   At the end of the run, use a circular motion to fill the crater.
6   Check the weld appearance:
    - Uneven surface profile or width means that the forward travel speed was irregular.
    - Undercut at the edges of the weld run can be caused by too short a dwell time or by a high current.
    - Pronounced ripples can result from an irregular weaving movement or a low current.
7   Deposit a second run in a similar fashion, but stop half way. Restart the arc at the front edge of the crater. As soon as the surface melts, move the arc to the back of the crater. Use a circular motion to form a weld pool over the crater and then resume forward movement.

Exercise 3

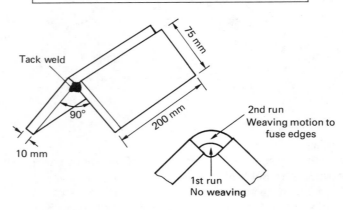

Skills acquired:	Controlling penetration
	Achieving inter-run fusion

Tack weld

75 mm

90°

200 mm

10 mm

2nd run
Weaving motion to fuse edges

1st run
No weaving

Fig. 7.7

Procedure:
1   Tack weld the two plates together at each end of the joint. Set up a root gap of 1 mm to 2 mm. Arrange the test piece so that the weld is deposited in the flat position.

2   Strike the arc on the tack weld and establish a weld pool.
3   Move the arc along the root. Adjust the speed so that the edges
    of the plate are just melted. Do not weave. A small weld bead is
    acceptable. The important aim is to achieve good root fusion
    and penetration.
4   Inspect the underside of the joint for uniformity of penetration.
    If a press is available, flatten the joint and examine the pen-
    etration bead for tearing which would indicate lack of fusion.
    ● Incomplete penetration and lack of fusion result from low
      current or excessively fast travel speed.
    ● A large penetration bead or burn-through indicate high
      current or slow travel speed.
5   When a satisfactory root run has been deposited, increase the
    current (MAG) or use a larger electrode (MMA) to deposit a
    second run and fill the groove. Use a weaving motion ensuring
    fusion into both the surface of the root run and the faces of the
    joint.
6   Cut a macrosection to check for both side and inter-run fusion.

Exercise 4

Skills acquired:	Achieving root fusion in a T-joint
	Controlling the profile of a fillet weld

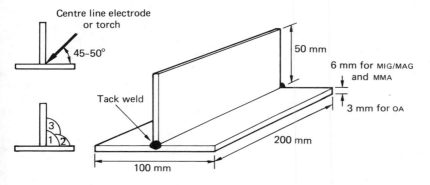

Fig. 7.8

Procedure:

1 Tack the plates together and clamp the test piece to the bench so that the joint is in the position shown in Fig. 7.8.

2 Strike the arc on the tack weld and establish a weld pool at one end of the joint. Set the current to about 130A for MAG or 110A for MMA welding.

3 Move the arc along the joint paying particular attention to achieving fusion of the plate surfaces, especially in the corner (*root*) of the joint. Do not try to deposit a large weld bead – 4 mm to 6 mm leg length is sufficient. Adjust the angle between the electrode and the plates to get uniform melting of the surfaces.

4 When the root run has been deposited, remove any slag and wire brush thoroughly.

5 Deposit the second run ensuring that the weld fuses into both the plate surface and the root run. A slight weaving action can be used and the current can be increased by 10A or 15A.

6 Deposit the third run to build up the weld profile.

7 Wire brush and inspect the finished weld.

   • Undercut at the edge of the weld indicates that the current was too high or the electrode angle was wrong.

   • Overlap or a badly shaped weld result from incorrect electrode angles.

   • Bulbous or rounded weld beads mean that the current was too low or the travel speed was too fast.

8 Use a fracture test (page 64) to check root fusion.

Exercise 5

Skills acquired: Controlling the weld pool in the vertical
                   position

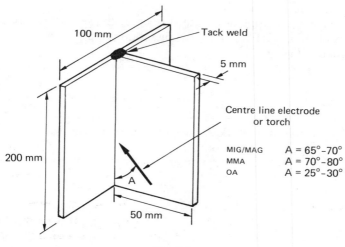

Fig. 7.9

Procedure:
1   Tack the plates together and fix them so that the joint line is
    vertical and at a comfortable height.
2   Strike the arc at the bottom edge of the joint. Keep the electrode
    at right angles to the joint line. As soon as the weld pool is
    established adjust the angle so that the electrode is pointing
    upwards as shown in Fig. 7.9. Use a current of about 100A.
3   Move up the joint, keeping the electrode directed at the root.
    Concentrate on achieving fusion, but do not allow the weld pool
    to become too large. Adjust electrode angle to give the best
    control of the pool. A slight forward and back movement may be
    useful.
4   Deposit a second run starting at the bottom and weaving across
    the face of the root run. Use the zig-zag movement practised in

Exercise 2 to move the weld pool from side to side. Pause at each side to get fusion into the plate surface.

5 With MAG welding, the root run can be deposited starting at the top of the joint. This is the vertical-down technique. Weld pool control is easier but there is a greater risk of lack of root fusion. The second run should be deposited vertically-up, weaving as necessary.

6 Pronounced rippling on the surface of the second run results from either an irregular weaving motion or a long pause at the edge of the weld.

Exercise 6

Skills acquired: Achieving root fusion in the vertical position

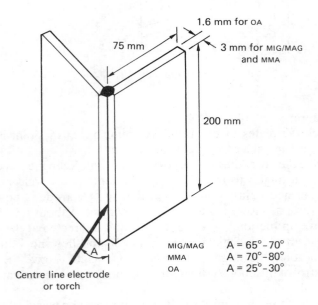

1.6 mm for OA

75 mm

3 mm for MIG/MAG and MMA

200 mm

MIG/MAG	A = 65°–70°
MMA	A = 70°–80°
OA	A = 25°–30°

A

Centre line electrode or torch

Fig. 7.10

Procedure:
1   Tack the plates together with a 2 mm gap in the root. Fix the test piece with the joint line vertical and in a comfortable position for welding.
2   Establish a weld pool at the lower end of the joint. Adjust the electrode angle and, using a small circular motion, melt the root faces. This gives a small onion shaped hole at the leading edge of the pool. Do not try to deposit a large bead. The objective is to fuse the root and achieve a uniform penetration bead.
3   Wire brush and examine the penetration bead. It should be about 2 mm high and uniform along the length of the joint. If the bead is large and looks like a collection of solidified droplets, either the current was too high or the travel speed was too slow.
4   Fill the remainder of the joint, using the vertical-up technique practised in Exercise 5.

Welder qualifications

Welders who have achieved a degree of proficiency and are welding on high quality work are often required to take an approval test. This is sometimes loosely referred to as **coding**. The approval test consists of producing a welded testpiece which is then inspected according to a standard specified by the client who is purchasing the fabrication. The test is repeated at intervals to check that the welder can still achieve the specified standard.

Typical standards are:

BS4871   applies to welders on pressure vessel or other high quality work.

BS4872   a lower standard test for general purpose work.

ASME IX   (ASME Nine) an American standard which is widely used for quality pipework in oil refineries.

HVCA   a standard issued by the Heating and Ventilating Constructors Association for workers in the construction industry particularly associated with central heating systems in large buildings.

From 1992 onwards there will be a CEN standard which will be in use in all countries of the EEC.

Approval tests are expensive and are usually arranged by an employer.

8

Working with MIG/MAG Welding

MIG/MAG welding is a popular choice for joining sheets, tubes and angle or box sections, but it can also produce high quality welds in plate. The skill needed to deposit simple welds is quickly acquired, making it attractive to novice welders. It does require, however, much practice to reach the skill levels necessary for quality welding on plate and pipe.

As a result of the popularity of the process, equipments have been designed to cater for a variety of interests. At one end of the range there are units which contain solid state circuits to control the arc and computerised memories which automatically set the welding conditions according to a pre-arranged schedule. These units can cost many thousands of pounds and contrast with the simple, low price MIG/MAG sets for garage and domestic use on sheet and thin plate or sections.

This wide choice of units makes selecting suitable equipment for MIG/MAG welding a difficult task. There is little point in purchasing an expensive, sophisticated unit for a straightforward task like making metal tool boxes. But it is highly undesirable to select a low cost set which may be underpowered for welding thick plate. One of the dangers of MIG/MAG welding is the ease with which welds can be deposited with an acceptable surface appearance but lacking proper fusion to the parent metal because insufficient power is available.

In this chapter we will start by establishing the essential characteristics of the power source and the wire drive system. These are key elements in the successful operation of the process. Later, we will look at some practical aspects of MIG/MAG welding.

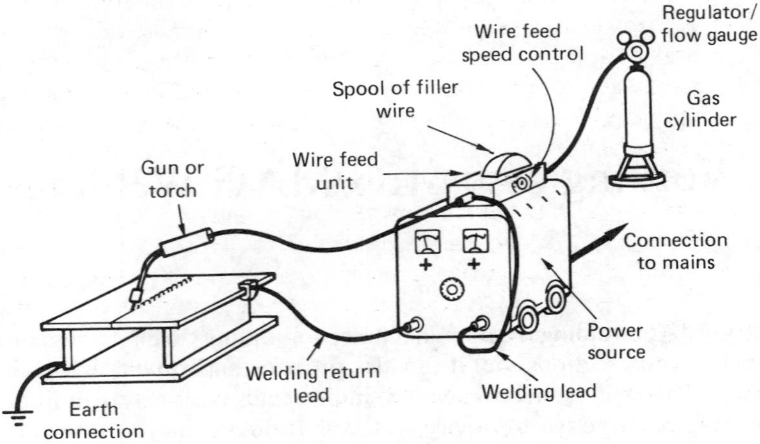

Fig. 8.1 Equipment for MIG/MAG welding

Power sources for MIG/MAG welding

Voltage output

The task of the power source in MIG/MAG welding is to control the arc length. To do this, it needs to keep the operating voltage constant because the arc length and arc voltage are directly related. Suppose the welder moves the nozzle a short distance away from the work. This could happen for a variety of reasons; for example, a jerky movement whilst adjusting the position of the body or muscle tiredness making it difficult to keep the hand movement steady. The arc length is immediately increased and the arc voltage rises in sympathy. The power source keeps the voltage constant at the value set by the welder at the beginning of the weld run. This forces the arc length to return to its pre-set value even if the welder has not restored the gun to its original distance from the work. In this way the arc length is corrected within one-hundredth of a second without any action on the part of the welder; in other words, it is **self adjusting**.

Power sources for MIG/MAG welding are constant voltage machines. This means that the voltage is selected by a control on the unit and remains more or less at that value throughout the welding operation. At the same time, the power source must be able to deliver whatever current the arc needs. As we will see later in the chapter, the amount of current drawn from the power source depends on the wire feed speed.

At its simplest, a MIG/MAG power source consists of a transformer and a rectifier. The latter is needed to convert the alternating current (a.c.) from the transformer to direct current (d.c.). MIG/MAG welding works most successfully with d.c. and to produce a stable arc the electrode is connected to the positive terminal of the power source. The transformer and rectifier, together with switches and fuses, are contained in a metal or plastic box and welding cable connections are usually mounted on the front for easy access.

The arc voltage is chosen to suit the application and the current. The transformer has a switched input so that a range of voltages can be selected according to arc requirements.

We have already noted that once selected, the voltage should remain constant. Although the machine will attempt to keep the operating voltage stable, it is influenced by the voltage of the electrical supply – the mains voltage. If the mains voltage increases, the voltage supplied to the arc increases in sympathy. For most work on sheet material the welder can compensate for changes in voltage resulting from mains fluctuations by moving faster or slower. But, when welding plate and pipe, voltage changes may alter the arc conditions sufficiently to cause lack of side and inter-run fusion. This is where the more expensive machines come into consideration as they are fitted with devices which sense the voltage changes and correct them within fractions of a second so that the arc does not have time to react and thus remains at the preset length.

High current operation

MIG/MAG operates best at high currents, that is above 300A for steel and 200A for aluminium. At these current levels the end of the electrode melts and forms small droplets which are propelled across the arc gap. They can only be seen with a slow motion camera and to the unaided eye it appears that the metal is being transferred as a fine spray.

For **spray transfer** to operate satisfactorily, the working voltage at the power source must be between 30 and 45V for steel, and 24 and 30V for aluminium.

The power source must also be capable of supplying the welding current continuously for periods up to 4 or 5 minutes. Why should we make this stipulation? Is it not sufficient to say that we want to weld at 300A or whatever?

The answer lies in the components used in the power source. Most of these, for example the rectifiers, have an electrical resistance. Although this is not very large, at the currents used in welding there is an appreciable heating effect similar to that of an electric fire. Cooling devices are incorporated in the power source but the designer of the unit is constrained by price and size. So a limit is placed on the time the current can flow before the temperature has reached danger level. When this time has expired the unit must be switched off to allow the components to cool. The higher the current the shorter the time it takes for the components to heat up to the critical point and vice versa.

The relationship between the time allowed for the current to flow and the cooling period is given by the **duty cycle**. By convention an overall time of 5 minutes has been adopted. So, a duty cycle of 60% means that there can be a maximum of 3 minutes continuous welding at the specified current. This must be followed by a cooling period of 2 minutes. At a lower current, the allowable welding time would be a larger portion of the 5 minute period and the duty cycle would be higher. As an example, the following figures have been quoted for one particular commercial unit:

Table 4
Duty cycles for typical MIG/MAG power source

Duty cycle	60%	80%	100%
Maximum current	350A	300A	270A
Maximum voltage	37V	35V	33V

It is common practice for a power source to be given an identification number by the manufacturer, e.g. XYZ350. This rarely indicates the maximum continuous current. More often than not it is the 60% duty cycle rating and the continuous current – 100% duty cycle – is appreciably lower. For most manual welding however, the 60% duty cycle rating is sufficient and is sometimes referred to as the continuous manual welding rating – three minutes welding is a long time!

Low current operation
There are many occasions when we want to weld at currents well below the spray transfer range. Unfortunately, at low currents, the arc in MIG/MAG welding becomes unstable. Molten metal collects as large globules on the end of the electrode and there is little or no melting of the surface of the workpiece.

With steel, the problem can be overcome by using a short arc length, i.e. a low arc voltage of around 20V, so that the tip of the electrode touches the weld pool before a globule can grow. In this way metal is transferred from the electrode to the weld pool about 50 to 100 times a second. The technique is called **dip transfer**.

The current rises when the tip touches the surface of the weld pool. If it increases too rapidly, small droplets of metal shoot from the arc (spatter). These stick to the surface of the joint. At the same time, the turbulence which these explosions cause in the weld pool give rise to a poor quality weld. To counteract this an **inductance** is included in the power source. An inductance is a coil of copper cable wound around an iron frame. Its effect is to resist changes in the welding current flowing through it. So, when the current starts to rise, the inductance acts against it and slows down the rate of change. Similarly when the current starts to fall, the inductance tries to keep the value at the higher level. This action is similar to that of the shock absorber in a car in dampening down any bouncing that comes from driving along a bumpy road.

In practice the best setting for the inductance is usually found by trial and error – there is no easy method of measuring the value. If the setting is too low, the short circuits are explosive and spatter is ejected. If there is too much inductance the weld becomes cold and the electrode stubs into the weld pool. At the optimum setting, the arc has a regular crisp sound and there is a minimum of spatter. Even under the best operating conditions there is usually a small amount of spatter. This can be tolerated since it does not affect the quality of the weld. The two problems it poses are blocking the gas nozzle, which therefore needs regular cleaning, and sticking to the surface of the parent metal. Both of these can be eased by coating the nozzle and the surfaces with an anti-spatter compound.

In units designed for use with the small diameter electrodes (0.6 and 0.8 mm) the inductance is usually fixed by the manufacturer at a value which gives acceptable results over the normal working range. With larger sets the welder can adjust the value of the inductance to give minimum spatter.

Dip transfer cannot be used with aluminium. If we want to work at low currents when MIG welding this metal we must adopt a different technique called **pulsed welding**. In this, the arc is kept alight by a low level background current. High current pulses are superimposed onto this background current at a rate of 50 per second. Each pulse detaches a small droplet so the arc behaves as if it were operating under spray transfer conditions. Special power sources are needed for pulse welding. In recent years these have been developed to include devices which 'read' what is happening in the arc and adjust the output accordingly – **synergic welding**, which can be used on both aluminium and steel in place of dip transfer.

Open circuit voltage

If a voltmeter is connected across the output terminals of a power source for MIG/MAG welding it will demonstrate that the voltage drops when welding starts. When no current is flowing, there is an open circuit. The voltage at the terminals is the **open circuit voltage** (OCV). As soon as the current flows, the resistance in the components of the power source causes a loss of voltage – this is the same resistance that leads to heating in the power source which we discussed earlier in this chapter.

The loss of voltage is about 2V for every 100A of current. So, if we want to weld aluminium at 200A with a voltage of 24 we need to start with an OCV of 28V, i.e.

24V (for the arc at 200A)

plus   4V (2×2) for the loss in the power source (2V per 100A)
equals **28V** with no current flow (i.e. OCV = 28V).

Again if the requirement was for 350A at 32V, for steel we would set the OCV at 39, i.e. $32 + (2 \times 3.5)$.

Voltage can also be lost in a welding circuit by bad connections. A loose nut on a terminal or bad contact between the return clamp and the work introduces further electrical resistance into the circuit. This causes a loss of voltage which may sometimes be detected by a rise in temperature at the connection.

Setting the OCV is not difficult if the power source is fitted with a voltmeter. Many low cost sets have only an indexed dial; this needs to be checked to see if it is calibrated for OCV or operating voltage. For good practice, a voltmeter should always be used to set the voltage on a MIG/MAG set.

Wire feed units

We have now seen that the arc length can be fixed by choosing the appropriate voltage on the power source. How can the current be set? To understand how this is done we must first look at the difference between wire feed speed and burn-off rate.

Wire feed speed is set at the motor on the drive unit and is under the control of the operator.

Burn-off rate is a measure of how fast the electrode is melting and this is decided by the level of current.

If the wire feed speed is greater than the burn-off rate the arc length gets progressively shorter until the tip of the electrode stubs into the weld pool. However, the power source is trying to keep the arc length at the setting selected by the welder (see page 119), so it delivers more current to increase the burn-off rate until it matches the wire feed speed.

This is another aspect of self-adjustment and it provides a means of adjusting the current. If a higher amperage is needed to get more heat into the joint, we simply increase the wire feed speed and the power source responds with a higher current to keep the arc length constant. There is a restriction to the amount of change we can make without adjusting the output voltage. In the previous section we saw that for a given OCV setting the output voltage falls by 2V for every 100A. Two volts is sufficient to produce a noticeable change in arc length. So, if we have increased the current by, say, 50A we should increase the OCV by 1V to keep the arc length at the original setting.

The burn-off rate depends not only on current but also on the diameter of the electrode wire. The smaller the diameter of the electrode, the longer the length melted off per minute by a given current. In other words, for the same current the wire feed must be faster for smaller electrode diameters.

Setting up MIG/MAG welding conditions

Possibly the most critical operation in MIG/MAG welding is setting up the welding conditions. This consists of choosing the optimum values for voltage, wire feed speed and inductance and setting the machine to maintain them during welding. If this is not done, even an experienced welder will have great difficulty in depositing a sound weld.

A typical setting up sequence for steel would be:

1   Choose dip or spray transfer.
    Dip transfer is preferred where the current is low, i.e. for welding sheet or for depositing welds in the overhead or vertical positions.

    Spray transfer is preferred for high current work on plates where the joint is in the flat position. It can also be used for horizontal-vertical fillet welds. It cannot be used for vertical or overhead positions on steel.

2   Choose wire diameter.
    Dip transfer – 0.6, 0.8 or 1.0 mm
    Spray transfer – 1.2 or 1.6 mm

    With smaller units there may be no choice. Many low cost units for the domestic market use only 0.6 mm diameter wire. For practical purposes, this places an upper limit of 100A on the welding current and it is inadvisable to try to weld steel which is thicker than 3.0 mm.

3   Set voltage approximately.
    Dip transfer   OCV = 22V
    Spray transfer OCV = 35V

4   Set wire drive control to mid position.

5   Set inductance approximately (if fitted).
    Dip transfer – mid position
    Spray transfer – either minimum position or switch out of circuit according to manufacturer's instructions.

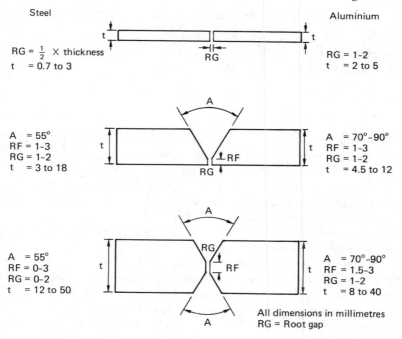

Steel

$RG = \frac{1}{2} \times$ thickness
t = 0.7 to 3

Aluminium

RG = 1–2
t = 2 to 5

A = 55°
RF = 1–3
RG = 1–2
t = 3 to 18

A = 70°–90°
RF = 1–3
RG = 1–2
t = 4.5 to 12

A = 55°
RF = 0–3
RG = 0–2
t = 12 to 50

A = 70°–90°
RF = 1.5–3
RG = 1–2
t = 8 to 40

All dimensions in millimetres
RG = Root gap

Fig. 8.2 Edge preparations for MIG/MAG welding

6 Make a test run on scrap plate.

Adjust voltage to give a stable arc – there should be no stubbing of the electrode into the weld pool and spatter should be at a minimum.

Adjust current to give the required weld size.

7 Examine the weld bead profile.

If the weld surface is high in the middle and does not blend in at the edges, the voltage is too low.

If the weld surface is very flat and the bead appears to wander from side to side, the voltage is too high.

If the weld is too large the wire feed speed is too high or the travel speed is too slow.

If there is excessive spatter adhering to the surface of the joint area, the inductance is too low.

8   Adjust the appropriate setting and deposit another test weld.

The setting up sequence for aluminium is similar, but only spray transfer can be used. The open circuit voltage is usually lower than that used for steel – 20V to 24V is typical.

Which gas?

The choice of a gas for shielding MIG/MAG welds is largely dictated by the material. For aluminium pure argon is the most commonly used gas. Copper needs a greater heat input and better results are obtained with helium or an argon-helium mixture. Good results can be obtained on stainless steel with argon to which a small amount of oxygen has been added. This addition, which amounts to 1% of the total volume, suppresses undercut at the edges of the weld which would be present with pure argon.

When steel is being welded we have a choice of gases – carbon dioxide (CO_2) or a mixture of this gas with argon. Neither of these can be said to be the best gas. Each has its advantages. CO_2 is cheaper and gives better penetration into the parent metal, but it produces more spatter and requires a higher voltage from the power source – this may not always be available. Argon-CO_2 (5% or 20%) is appreciably more expensive but gives a superior finish to the surface of the weld and is almost spatter free. Both give sound welds provided the equipment has been set up properly.

Which filler?

The composition of the electrode or filler wire must be matched to the metal being welded.

For steel, the main consideration is strength. With critical work, the choice is based on trials and the filler is specified as part of the weld procedure. On more general work with mild and low carbon steel, guidance can be obtained from the supplier.

Filler wires for steel can be either solid or they can have a flux core. The latter are available only in the larger diameters and their selection depends on a number of factors including position of welding, steel composition, and economics.

The choice of a filler for aluminium alloys is often more difficult. Strength is again an important factor but in many cases crack prevention is the prime consideration (see page 79).

9

Working with Manual Metal Arc Welding

Compared with the MIG/MAG process, the equipment required for MMA welding is simple. All that is needed is a power supply unit, cables and an electrode holder. The capital cost is low, and this in itself is often sufficient reason for choosing MMA welding. Another factor which favours MMA welding is its versatility. By simply changing the type of electrode, a wide range of metals can be welded using the same equipment.

On the other hand, we have already seen in Chapter 2 that there are some drawbacks, not the least being the higher skill level which is required. The operation of the process can be made significantly easier if attention is paid first to the suitability of the power source and then to the choice of the best electrode.

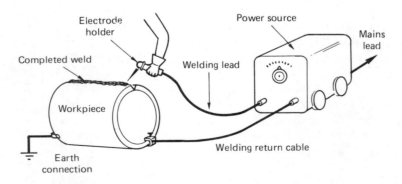

Fig. 9.1   Equipment for MMA welding

Power supplies for MMA welding

Before starting, we should remind ourselves of the three essential functions of a power source for MMA welding: it must

- isolate the welder from the mains to avoid electric shock
- provide the voltage required to strike the arc
- supply current at the value fixed by the welder, over the range of operating voltages.

The problems of electric shock and the role of the power source in protecting the welder against contact with the mains voltage were studied in Chapter 6. The two remaining functions need to be considered in more detail, but first we must decide which type of current we are going to use.

A.C. or D.C.?

MMA welding works with both alternating current (a.c.) and direct current (d.c.). This is not to say that all MMA electrodes work with both types of current. Some electrodes only work with d.c. or only with a.c. whilst there are makes which work with both. The choice of type of current may be influenced by operating factors, but it is difficult to dissociate it from electrode considerations. The electrode may be specified for a particular job because it gives the desired properties to the joint. If it is an electrode which only works on d.c. the choice of current is made for us. On the other hand if the only power supply available is an a.c. unit, we must select an electrode which is capable of running with this type of current.

One of the main advantages of a.c. is freedom from **arc blow**. This is a form of arc instability which occurs with d.c. welding. The arc is dragged to one side by magnetic forces set up by the welding current (Fig. 9.2). Its effects can be minimised by positioning the welding return clamp at the end of the joint so that the current flows along the line of the weld. With modern flux formulations, arc blow is less of a problem, but there are still a number of the older type of electrode in use. The easier answer is to change to a.c.

The other principal advantage of a.c. is the use of low cost power units. The power source for a.c. is a simple transformer fitted with some means of adjusting the current output. Such a unit requires very little maintenance. In contrast, d.c. units are more complex. At

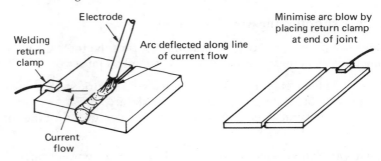

Electrode

Welding
return
clamp

Arc deflected along line
of current flow

Minimise arc blow by
placing return clamp
at end of joint

Current
flow

Fig. 9.2 Arc blow with d.c. welding

one time, motor generators were the only source of d.c. for MMA welding. These are still used on site work where they can be driven by a petrol or diesel engine thus making the welder independent of local electricity supplies. For shop use, transformer-rectifiers have become common and the introduction of solid state devices has made these units flexible and very reliable. Both generators and transformer-rectifier units are appreciably more expensive than a power source for a.c. welding, so it is reasonable to examine the advantages of d.c.

The first consideration is that d.c. is safer than a.c. and for this reason alone is preferred for site work. High open circuit voltages are needed to strike an arc on a.c. Often these are in excess of 80V which make them potentially dangerous, especially in damp conditions. With d.c., electrodes are available which strike at not much more than 60V. Secondly, a wider range of electrodes can be developed for d.c., many of which are easier to use than the equivalent a.c. versions. Applications such as hardfacing may only be done with d.c. Finally, leaving aside arc blow, the arc in d.c. welding is more stable in that there is less risk of it being extinguished during an accidental touch down. With a.c., the voltage is continuously changing from zero to maximum volts one hundred times per second. If the welder touches the electrode onto the surface of the weld pool or the plate, the arc goes out. There may be insufficient voltage available at that instant from the power source to restrike the arc with the result that the weld pool solidifies and it is difficult to detach the electrode. With d.c. the voltage is steady at the working level and the full OCV is available should the arc be instantaneously extinguished.

Current ranges

The level of current used depends on the thickness. This in turn determines the size of electrode which should be used. The size of an electrode is the diameter of the core wire.

Electrodes are manufactured in specific sizes which may be quoted in millimetres, or gauge size.

Table 5
Electrode sizes for MMA welding

Metric (mm)	Gauge (swg)
1.6	16
2.5	12
3.25	10
4.0	8
5.0	6
6.0*	
6.3	4

*Note: There is no direct swg equivalent for 6.0 mm

For each size of electrode there is an optimum current range. The lower end of the range is the minimum current for stable operation. If the electrode is used below this level it is difficult to avoid stubbing, or touch down, and arc extinction.

The upper limit is set by the amount of heat generated in the core wire. Steel has an appreciable electrical resistance. When the welding current passes along the core wire, it offers a resistance to the flow. The energy used in overcoming this resistance is converted to heat, just as in the heating element of an electric fire. The resistance of steel is less than that of the nickel-chromium wire used in the heater, but the heating effect is still appreciable.

The amount of heating also depends on the current level. The higher the current, the more heat that is developed. If the current is too high, the heat from the core starts to damage the flux covering and it ceases to operate effectively. Using an electrode which is being overheated results in slag inclusions and porosity in the weld and a loss of alloying elements which are needed for strength. The danger level for the current depends on the diameter of the core wire. Larger diameters can carry more current before the heating effect becomes critical. There is always the temptation to over-run the electrode because to do so gives faster welding speeds, but quality is sacrificed and it is always better to change to the next larger size of electrode.

Table 6
Current ranges for MMA steel electrodes

Electrode size (mm)	Current (Amp)	
	Minimum	Maximum
2.5	50	90
3.2	65	130
4.0	110	185
5.0	150	250
6.0	200	315
6.3	220	350

Where a square edge preparation is being used, i.e. with sheet and thin plate, the current depends on the thickness.

Table 7
Typical currents for MMA welding of sheet

Metal thickness		Current (Amp)
(mm)	(in)	
1.6	1/16	30–50
3.2	1/8	70–90
5.0	3/16	90–110
6.3	1/4	100–140

With V and U preparations, the current is matched to the size of electrode being used and the position of welding. For example, a typical weld sequence for a single-V butt joint in 18 mm plate in the flat position would be:

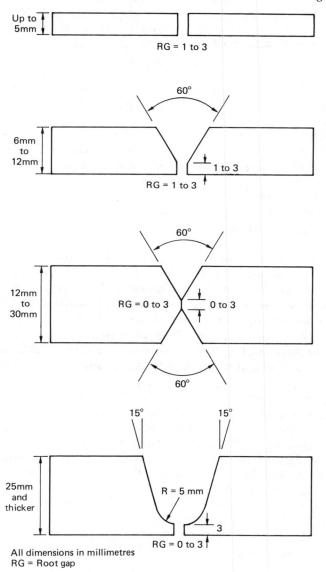

All dimensions in millimetres
RG = Root gap

Fig. 9.3   Edge preparations for MMA welding of steel

Root run		3.2 mm electrode at 95A
Filling passes		5.0 mm 200A
Capping pass		5.0 mm 240A
	or	6.3 mm 270A

For the same size electrodes, the current would be reduced by about 20% if the joint is in the vertical position.

Specifications for power sources

From what has been said so far we can see that the three main items in a specification for a power source for MMA welding are:

1   Type of current: a.c. or d.c.
2   Open circuit voltage
3   Maximum current output

Unlike the power sources used in MIG/MAG welding, the OCV of a MMA unit is fixed. It must be chosen to match the requirements of the electrodes being used. This offers few problems with the larger industrial units designed to work from a 390–440V supply. With the smaller power sources operating at 240V (13A) input the OCV is limited by the design. If the OCV is too low, the arc will not only be reluctant to strike, it will also be liable to stubbing and extinction. This is more of a problem with transformer units for a.c. welding.

When we come to specify the current rating the points we discussed in the chapter on MIG/MAG welding apply equally to MMA welding. We need to know the duty cycle for the stated current output. Standard MMA electrodes have a length of 420 mm of which 380 mm can be used. It takes some 2 to 3 minutes to melt an electrode operating at the mid-point of the current range for the size. If the duty cycle is calculated on the basis of a 5 minute period, the 60% duty cycle rating gives the current we can draw from the power source continuously over 3 minutes. If we take this as the maximum current we can use when melting the complete 380 mm length of an electrode, there will always be a margin of power in hand.

Information about OCV, current rating and duty cycles should be given on a plate or panel attached to the power source. Mention has been made above of 240V units. Many welding problems with these can be traced to inadequate voltage or current ratings.

The current controls on most power sources for MMA welding are marked with the output values. Some smaller sets simply give minimum and maximum positions with an uncalibrated scale. This is adequate for many applications where the welder can adjust the setting to give an arc which can be comfortably controlled whilst being able to fuse the joint faces. But, for high quality work or for reproducibility an ammeter is needed to set the current accurately.

Electrodes for MMA welding

In Chapter 2, some of the functions of the flux which covers a MMA electrode were described and it was indicated that the chemical composition governs the operating characteristics and the properties of the weld metal. We need to take a closer look at the flux composition if we are to choose the best electrode for any given application.

There are three main flux systems in use with currently available electrodes:

- **Rutile**, which is mainly titanium oxide. This type of flux gives easy control of the weld pool. The slag is readily detached to reveal a smooth surface to the weld. Rutile covering provides good general purpose electrodes which satisfy most requirements for welding mild steel. They do not give high strength and they deposit weld metal which is relatively high in hydrogen even after they have been dried. So, rutile electrodes are not generally suitable for welding steels which are prone to HAZ cracking (see page 71). If they do have to be used for this purpose, the steel needs to be pre-heated to at least 175°C and kept at this temperature during welding to avoid cracking.
- **Cellulosic** coverings give an arc which penetrates about twice as deep as rutile for the same current. These electrodes are not as easy to use as rutile and find more favour in America than in Europe. They are widely accepted for the welding of pipelines.
- **Basic** electrodes are recommended for welding steels which suffer from HAZ cracking. They can be dried to give a low hydrogen content which is an essential requirement for successful welding of crack sensitive steels. The flux composition

enables alloying elements to be added to the molten pool which give the weld metal high strength.

The term **basic** can be misleading since it normally implies simplicity; in this context, it refers to a chemical condition which is the opposite to acidic. Basic electrodes are not easy to use. The arc length must be kept short and the flux can be difficult to control. The slag may not detach easily and the surface of the weld shows distinct rippling.

Iron powder electrodes are not a class by themselves, but are a variant on either rutile or, occasionally, basic types. Iron powder is added to the flux to increase the melting rate and so allow higher speeds of welding. It also makes the arc easier to operate and for this reason iron powder electrodes are very attractive to the novice. There is a danger, however, in their high melting rates. If the travel speed is not fast enough or if the electrode angle is wrong, molten metal floods over the joint faces before they have been properly melted by the arc. This results in lack of side-fusion. The danger is particularly severe in welding T-joints.

Iron powder electrodes are particularly useful in depositing fillet welds in decorative work as the slag detaches easily and the weld has a very smooth surface. They also have a pleasing profile, especially when painted.

Selecting the most suitable electrode

Choosing between the three main types of MMA electrode is not difficult. For the majority of work with steel, a rutile electrode suffices. Basic electrodes would only be chosen if the steel is a high strength grade or is crack sensitive. A cellulosic electrode could be used in place of rutile in a number of situations and most American textbooks recommend them. It is unlikely that they would be preferred in the UK where they are confined to more specialised applications.

The next step is not so straightforward. It involves matching the operating characteristics of the electrode to the job on hand. Universal electrodes are available which weld in all positions on both a.c. and d.c. but they may well represent a compromise. Possibly they are not as fast in the flat position as an electrode designed specifically for that task. Maybe the surface profile of a fillet weld is more convex than would be desirable. The slag may be viscous – sticky – and not easily controlled. These compromises may be acceptable when there is a variety of work or there is only an infrequent demand for welding. In these cases it would be uneconomic to stock a number of different, little used types of electrode. In a busy welding shop, on the other hand, it could well be worthwhile purchasing, say, an electrode designed just for d.c. welding in the flat position if most of the work is done that way.

When we turn to the sales list to make our choice we will probably find that there is a collection of trade names which tell us little about the characteristics of the electrode. To overcome this, electrodes are given a code number. There are two coding systems in use in the UK to describe electrodes for the welding of carbon steels. The first is covered by British Standard BS639:1986 and is based on the recommendations of the International Standards Organisation (ISO). The second is a United States code AWS 5.1 which has been designed by the American Welding Society.

The BS639 code for a typical rutile electrode is:

E4322 R 30

The code can be divided into three sections:

E4322 Indicates the minimum tensile properties and impact values. An E43 electrode has a minimum tensile strength of $410N/mm^2$ and is suitable for use with BS4360 Grades 40 and 43 steels. An E51 electrode with a minimum strength of $510N/mm^2$ would be needed for Grade 50 and other higher strength steels. The last two digits (i.e. 22 in this example) are of interest to the designer of structures where there is a risk of brittle fracture since they give details of the values obtained in impact tests.

R Defines the type of flux covering:
R = rutile; C = cellulosic; B = basic

30 Gives information about the operating characteristics. The first digit defines the possible positions of welding, whilst the second defines the electrical requirements. In this case:
3 = electrode can be used in the flat and, for fillet welds, horizontal-vertical positions.
0 = Not suitable for a.c.

Table 8
BS639 – Position and electrical digit

First Digit		Second Digit		
Code	Position	Code	D.C. polarity	A.C. OCV
		0	Refer to manufacturer	Not suitable for a.c.
1	All	1	+ or −	50
2	All except V-down	2	−	50
3	F and H-V (fillet)	3	+	50
4	F only	4	+ or −	70
5	F; V-down; H-V (fillet)	5	−	70
		6	+	70
		7	+ or −	90
		8	−	90
		9	+	90

Note the high OCV corresponding to Codes 7, 8 and 9. It is unlikely that this would be available on small portable transformer units so these electrodes would be unsuitable for use with them.

The code number can contain other information. If there is iron powder in the coating the amount can be indicated in the code immediately after the letter designating the type of flux:

E4322 R **120** 30

The 120 tells us that the recovery rate is 120%. In other words, the amount of metal deposited is 20% greater than the weight of core metal melted. The extra metal comes from iron powder added to the flux covering.

Finally, the inclusion of the letter H at the end of the code shows that the electrode is capable of being dried to give a hydrogen content which is low enough for the welding of high strength steels:

E5154 B 24 **H**

The significance of the hydrogen content was discussed in Chapter 5.

The AWS equivalent to an E5154 B 24 H electrode would be:

E7016

With this code we have two groups. As with the BS639 code, the first two digits indicate tensile strength but in this case it is in pounds per square inch. An E60 electrode gives a minimum strength of 60,000 psi and is equivalent to a BS639:E43 electrode, whilst an E70, which has a strength of 70,000 psi, is more or less the same as an E51 in the BS639 Code. Note that the AWS code does not include impact values.

The last two digits in the code are concerned with the type of flux, position of welding and electrical characteristics:

Table 9
AWS Electrode Code – third digit: welding position

Code	Applicable positions
E--1-	flat, horizontal, vertical and overhead
E--2-	flat and horizontal fillet
E--4-	flat, horizontal, overhead and vertical-down

Table 10
AWS Electrode Code – fourth digit: electrode usage

Code	Current	Coating
E---0	d.c.+	Cellulose, sodium
E---1	a.c., d.c.+	Cellulose, potassium
E---2	a.c., d.c.−	Rutile, sodium
E---3	a.c., d.c.+ or −	Rutile, potassium
E---4	a.c., d.c.+ or −	Rutile, iron powder
E---5	d.c.+	Basic, sodium
E---6	a.c., d.c.+	Basic, potassium
E---7	a.c., d.c.−	Iron oxide, iron powder
E---8	a.c., d.c.+	Basic, iron powder

10

Oxy-fuel Gas Systems

Oxy-acetylene (OA) welding was once used widely for the joining of sheets, thin plate and sections. It was applied to the fabrication of water storage tanks, sheet metal work in the car and domestic appliance manufacturing industries and to the jointing of pipework systems. Over the years it has been replaced in production work by MIG/MAG and TIG. The reasons for this are complex but probably the most telling is its slowness. Output per welder is low and slow welding speeds encourage buckling of the sheet around the joint, involving costly post-weld straightening. Oxy-acetylene welding also requires a high level of skill if satisfactory results are to be obtained especially on butt joints in sheet. It is interesting to note that one of the few remaining uses of the process in production is the welding of steel pipes with diameters of 50 mm or less. Manoeuvring a MIG/MAG gun or an MMA electrode around this small diameter is difficult, whereas a skilled oxy-acetylene welder can produce an acceptable joint with good penetration even under difficult conditions of access such as would occur in complex pipework fabrications. A unique use of the oxy-acetylene process is for the welding of lead in the plumbing and roofing industries, and for the lead lining of acid storage tanks. It is often called lead burning.

In contrast to this situation, oxy-acetylene welding still finds a place in the smaller, jobbing shop where the versatility of the equipment is an attraction. In addition to welding, the basic equipment can be modified for cutting or heating applications using a range of gases other than acetylene (Fig. 10.1).

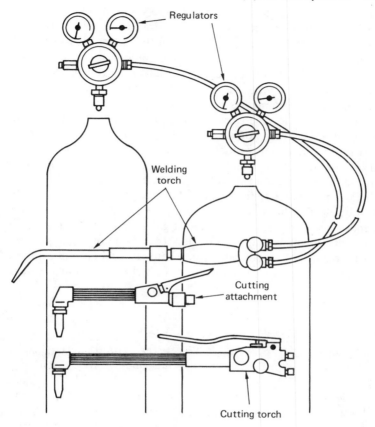

Fig. 10.1 Oxy-acetylene welding and cutting equipment

Oxy-acetylene welding practice

In Chapter 7 we looked at the structure of the oxy-acetylene welding flame and highlighted the need to get the balance between the two gases correct. We also noted that the hottest part of the flame is at the tip of the inner cone. It is important to distinguish between the temperature of the flame and the amount of heat it can supply to the joint. In all correctly adjusted oxy-acetylene flames, the temperature at the hottest point is between 3100°C and 3500°C. However, the heat input is not always the same because it depends on the volume of gases being burnt. This is another way of saying that the heating effect depends on the size of the flame. For thin sheet only a relatively small amount of heat is needed to get fusion of the joint faces, so a small flame suffices – a butt joint in 3 mm wall pipe calls for a much larger flame.

The mixed gases are carried through a nozzle. The hole in the nozzle must be large enough to carry the volume of gas required. On the other hand, if only a small volume of gases is flowing through a large hole, the flame is likely to be unstable. The manufacturer of gas welding equipment therefore provides a range of nozzle sizes which can be matched to the flame size needed for the joint. Rather than quote the diameter of the hole, the nozzle is given an index number according to the amount of gas it can carry. The number originally gave a rough indication of the amount of gas used measured in cubic feet per hour. Thus a number 2 nozzle used 2 ft³/hr. The metric unit is litres/hour (1 ft³/hr = 28.3 l/hr).

Table 11
Typical nozzle sizes for welding steel sheet

| Steel thickness | | Nozzle | Gas flow rate | Filler diameter |
mm	swg	number	litres/hour	mm
0.9	20	1	25–35	1.6
1.2	18	2	50–65	1.6
1.6	16	3	70–90	1.6
2.4	12	5	130–150	2.4 or 3.2
3.2	10	7	200–220	3.2
4.0	8	10	270–290	3.2

This table indicates some typical conditions for welding sheet steel. There is considerable overlap between nozzles and the range of thicknesses could be covered by fewer nozzles. For example, a number 2 nozzle could be used for 0.9, 1.2 and 1.6 mm.

The gas flow rates are of interest because they give a guide to the amount of acetylene and oxygen needed to make a weld. Flow rates are not metered in normal welding practice. The correct flame size is obtained by first setting the regulators to the value recommended in the equipment handbook for the size of nozzle. The controls on the blowpipe are then adjusted until the flame is neutral (see page 104). It is then tested by melting a spot on some scrap sheet. The blowpipe controls can be readjusted to give a manageable flame.

Safety with oxy-acetylene welding

General aspects of safety in welding were discussed in Chapter 6 and apply equally to using the oxy-acetylene process. There are two aspects which are unique to oxy-acetylene welding and warrant special attention.

Back fire	Sometimes the flame burns up the nozzle and back to the body of the blowpipe – recognised by a staccato, crackling sound. This may happen because the flame is too small for the nozzle size or the hole is blocked by spatter or slag. More often than not, the back fire extinguishes the flame which can be re-ignited in the usual way. If the back fire persists, the body of the blowpipe can be damaged. The valves must be closed – oxygen first – and the blowpipe plunged into water to cool it. The conditions of the hose, the nozzle and its seating should be checked before lighting up again.
Flashback	If the flame spreads beyond the body of the blowpipe (a flashback) the hoses and regulators may be damaged. Flashback arrestors should be fitted to minimise the risk. Such devices may be described in sales literature as flame traps.
Hose connectors	The thread on connectors used for the acetylene hose are left-handed as opposed to right-handed for oxygen. This avoids the risk of confusion. The connectors at the blowpipe end of the hoses should be fitted with non-return valves (hose protectors or hose check valves).
Cylinders	The general remarks given in Chapter 6 about the safe use of cylinders apply to oxy-acetylene welding. But, acetylene imposes further require-

ments. Cylinders must be upright in use as they contain a liquid in which the acetylene is dissolved.

Welding procedures

When welding sheet and thin material, say less than 5 mm, it is not difficult to supply sufficient heat to the joint and a leftward or forehand technique is employed for OA welding. In this, the blowpipe is pointed in the direction of welding, preheating the unfused edges (Fig. 10.2a). This enables faster welding which is essential to reduce the spread of heat and so combat distortion. Using slow travel speeds with a leftward technique results in excessive distortion in the sheet.

If additional metal is needed to build up the profile of the joint it is added as a filler wire. Typically the diameter is either 1.6 mm or 3.2 mm. The wire is introduced into the weld pool where it is fused by the heat in the molten metal. It is not melted in the flame and then dropped onto the work as this would take heat away from the joint faces and cause lack of fusion.

In a V-joint, there is a danger that metal will flow forward between the unfused root faces with the leftward technique and it is often helpful to raise the far end of the joint so that the work surface is inclined at an angle of 10°.

On thicker material – 5 mm and above – a rightward or backhand technique is preferred. In this the blowpipe is pointed at the weld pool, i.e. the opposite way to the direction of welding (Fig. 10.2b). This concentrates heat between the joint faces in a V-joint and, at the same time, holds back the molten metal so that the welder has a clear view of the root faces. Rightward welding is faster than leftward and consumes less gas. The angle of the V-preparation can also be reduced giving savings in filler metal.

Steel can be readily welded by the oxy-acetylene process without the need for flux. The gases from the flame provide adequate protection against atmospheric contamination.

Stainless steel and aluminium, on the other hand, need a flux first to clear the joint of oxides and then to protect the weld metal. The flux is applied to the joint as a paste before welding and is coated onto the filler wire by the welder. Fluxes used in OA welding are corrosive and must be completely removed after welding otherwise they will cause damage to the joint if they become moist in service. For this reason, and because a high degree of skill is needed, OA welding is not often used for the welding of stainless steel and aluminium.

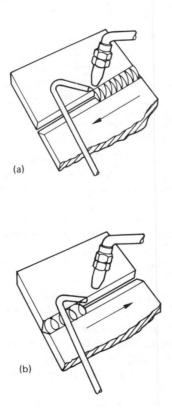

Fig. 10.2 Oxy-acetylene welding techniques

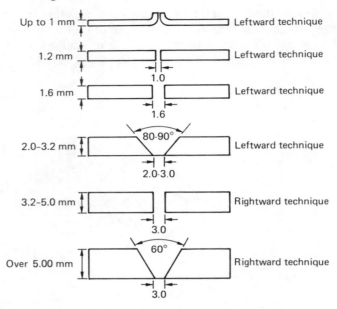

Fig. 10.3   Edge preparations for OA welding

Braze welding

Occasionally it would be useful to deposit a fillet weld without fusing the surfaces of the joint. One situation where this would be an advantage was mentioned in Chapter 5 – the welding of cast iron. Another case would be welding copper plate or pipe where, due to the high thermal conductivity, the heat flows rapidly from the joint area making it difficult to raise the temperature of the metal to melting point.

Braze welding satisfies this need. The traditional and more common name for the technique is bronze welding but in recent years braze welding has been adopted as the standard term.

In strict terms braze welding is not welding, but the technique used is similar to oxy-acetylene welding although without the parent metal fusion. Instead, as the parent metal remains solid, the molten filler flows freely over it and so wets the surfaces of the joint. This wetting action needs a covering of molten flux to work successfully.

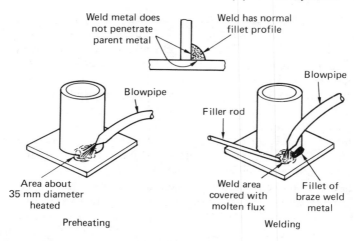

Fig. 10.4 Braze welding

In many ways the role of the flux is similar to that of a detergent to make water flow over greasy plates.

The joint is set up as for welding. But, because it is easier to wet clean surfaces, particular attention must be given to the preparation of the joint. Thorough degreasing and wire brushing is essential. The surfaces of the joint are coated with a flux just before starting to make the bronze weld.

The first step is to heat an area to a temperature at which the filler metal just melts when touched onto the plate. The parent metal must not be fused. Mixing parent metal and bronze filler could lead to cracks in the finished weld. The filler is coated with flux to ensure that there is always sufficient present to maintain the wetting action. Filler is added to the joint area until the desired fillet size is obtained and the blowpipe is then moved forward depositing the fillet in a similar way to OA welding.

When the weld is completed, all flux must be removed with hot water. Damp flux is corrosive and could attack the metal in service.

Oxy-fuel gas cutting

Iron burns in oxygen. This is difficult to visualise if we think of burning simply in terms of the combustion of paper, coal or gas. Flames are, of course, associated with the process of burning but they are not an inevitable feature. Burning is a common name for the chemical reaction of oxidation. When iron combines with oxygen heat is given off – in chemical terms it is an exothermic reaction. Before this reaction can take place the iron has to be hot. The minimum temperature at which the reaction occurs is called the **oxygen ignition temperature**.

This reaction is the key to oxy-fuel gas cutting of steel; in some industries the operator of the cutting torch is called a 'burner'. The principles of the process are shown in Fig. 10.5.

A preheat flame is needed to keep the surface of the steel above the oxygen ignition temperature. The chemical (exothermic) reaction between the iron in the steel and the oxygen cutting jet generates enough heat within the cut to keep the reaction going. But if the surface cools as the cold oxygen hits it, the reaction ceases. The preheat flame provides just enough heat to offset this. If the flame is too large, the top of the cut is widened and a rounded edge is produced.

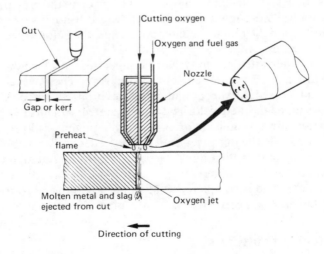

Fig. 10.5   Principles of oxygen-fuel gas cutting

The shank or handle of a cutting blowpipe is similar to that used for welding. The welding nozzle is replaced by an assembly which has pipes to carry the gases for the preheat flame and a pipe for the cutting oxygen. The latter is fitted with a hand operated valve which allows the operator to supply the cutting oxygen when the preheat flame has raised the surface of the steel to the ignition temperature.

As with welding, the size of a cutting nozzle is related to the volume of gases it carries. The nozzle incorporates both the pre-heat and cutting orifices. Most modern nozzles are made from one piece of copper, but a few are constructed in two pieces which are assembled together when they are attached to the shank.

Cuts can be made either square to the top surface or at an angle to produce a bevel, as would be needed for a V-preparation. With bevel cutting the effective thickness of the cut is greater than the actual thickness of the plate and allowance needs to be made for this in selecting a nozzle and cutting conditions.

The quality of a cut is influenced by a number of variables. The effects of these are illustrated in Fig. 10.6.

Which gas?

Although acetylene is the gas which is most commonly associated with welding and cutting there are a number of other equally important gases, at least as far as cutting is concerned.

Welding offers us very little choice. Except on very thin material only acetylene gives the minimum flame temperature needed to guarantee good fusion and sound weld metal. With steel below 1.0 mm thick, acceptable welds can be made using gases such as methylacetylene, butadiene and ethylene or commercial products based on these and sold under trade names, e.g. MAP. Propane or natural gas rarely give good results; even welds which look good on the surface fail a simple bend test. Hydrogen has been used to weld aluminium but the welds tend to be porous and the gas poses safety hazards in handling and storage.

Cutting imposes fewer restrictions since the temperature of the preheat flame is not so critical – the aim is to heat the steel, not to melt it. Acetylene, propane, butane and natural gas, as well as a number of commercial products can be used. Advantages are

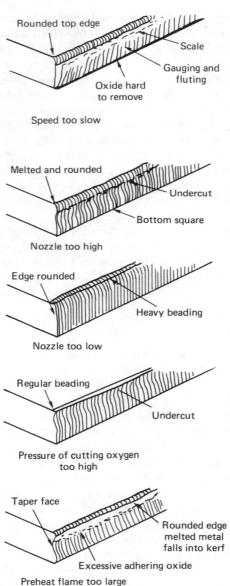

Fig. 10.6 Cutting faults

claimed for each and these must be assessed for any particular application. The nozzle design is not the same for all these gases and must be matched not just for optimum results but also in the interests of safety.

Oxygen used for cutting must have a high degree of purity. Low grade gas slows down, and may even stop, the cutting action. Only oxygen supplied for oxy-fuel gas cutting should be used. At the same time great care must be taken to avoid badly fitted connections in the oxygen line which would cause air to be introduced, thus contaminating the gas.

11

Resistance Welding Sheet Metal

Resistance welding is usually associated with mass production of sheet metal components. We would see numerous examples of resistance welding if we were to take a walk around a car body plant or a factory making washing machines or office furniture. This would be a very narrow view of the process. It plays an important role in many other industries. A good example is the manufacture of jet engines for aircraft. Combustion chambers and outer shells are welded to very high standards with resistance welding techniques.

In each of these applications a large number of spot welds is involved. The conditions can be set by carrying out a number of trial runs on test pieces taken from the same sheet as the component. All that is needed then is to make periodic checks to see that the settings have not changed.

This is only part of the story, however. One of the major attributes of resistance welding is its ability to repeat the selected conditions from one weld to the next. This provides the basis for a quality control system which is attractive to the manufacturers of critical components in, say, stainless steels or nickel heat-resisting alloys.

There are also a number of applications for resistance welding in the jobbing sheet metal workshop – a typical product is ducting for ventilation systems. Although not really suitable for making single welds it does offer a useful method of jointing where the number of welds justify the time spent establishing optimum conditions. The exact number depends on local conditions but is typically about thirty to forty.

Equipment for resistance welding

The principal components of a resistance welding system are shown in Fig. 11.1.

Larger machines tend to be static – fixed in one position in the welding shop – and the work is brought to them. They have electronic circuits to control the welding current and the pressure is applied to the electrodes by air or hydraulic rams. Components for a jet engine would be welded on a static machine. In volume production, these large machines may contain a number of pairs of electrodes so that many spot welds can be made on the component at the same time.

There are situations, however, where it is more convenient to move the electrodes to the work – on a production line or in a car repair workshop to quote two extremes. Portable units are available for these situations, but inevitably are of lower power and lack the sophisticated controls of the larger static machine (Fig. 11.2).

Industrial units are connected to a 390/440V single phase mains supply, although a step down transformer may be used for portable units in the interests of safety. Small portable spot welders for use in garages and for DIY work are designed to work from a 240V (13A) supply. They are inevitably of lower power and there is a limitation on the maximum thickness of sheet they can handle.

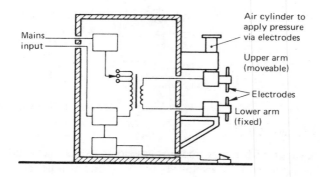

Fig. 11.1   Components of a resistance spot welder

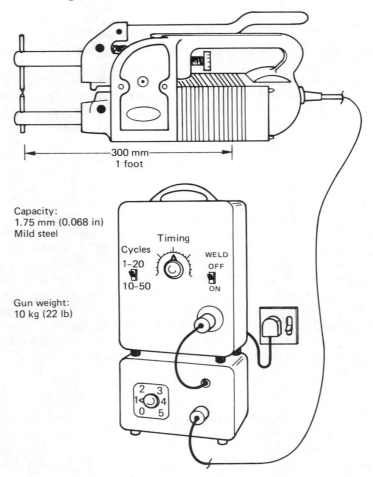

Fig. 11.2 Portable spot welder

Welding sequence

The overall time for a typical spot weld is usually less than one second. It is measured in **cycles** – one cycle is one fiftieth of a second. This unit is used because it corresponds to the frequency of the power supply. Resistance welding uses a.c. which goes from zero to a positive current through zero to a negative current and back to zero fifty times per second.

The easiest way to understand what happens in spot welding is to look at a typical welding sequence.

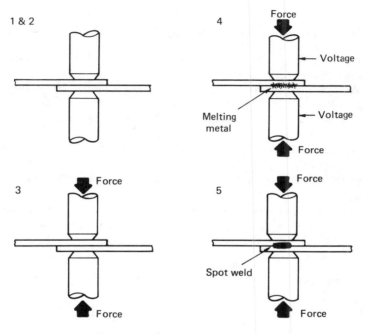

Fig. 11.3 Spot welding sequence

1 The overlapping sheets are placed in the gap between the electrodes and aligned so that the weld is made in the correct position.
2 The electrodes are brought together, closing the gap and gripping the workpieces.
3 Force is applied to the electrodes for about 20 cycles giving very close contact between the sheets at a point on the interface (**squeeze time**).
4 The welding voltage is applied to the electrodes and the current flows through the work via the electrodes to melt the metal at the

interface. The number of cycles needed (**weld time**) depends on the thickness of the material.

5   When the current has been switched off by the timer, the pressure is maintained for about 50 cycles while the weld solidifies and cools (**forge time**).

What makes an acceptable weld?

There are two techniques that can be used to check if a weld is acceptable.

We can make a vertical slice along the centreline of the joint and etch the cross-section. This reveals the shape of the weld nugget (see page 65). Using a ruler and a magnifying glass, the critical dimensions of the weld can be measured (Fig. 11.4).

Notice the depressions in the surfaces of the sheets. These are the imprints of the electrodes made during the forge time. They show that the force was being correctly applied while the weld was solidifying.

A much easier way of checking the weld is to do a peel test (Fig. 11.5). In this, one sheet is gripped with a pair of pliers and is rolled

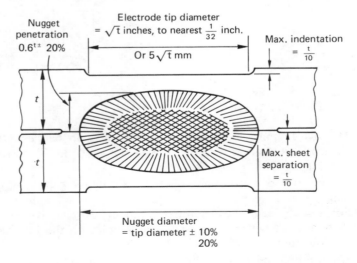

Nugget penetration
$0.6^{t} \pm 20\%$

Electrode tip diameter
$= \sqrt{t}$ inches, to nearest $\frac{1}{32}$ inch.
Or $5\sqrt{t}$ mm

Max. indentation
$= \frac{t}{10}$

t

t

Max. sheet separation
$= \frac{t}{10}$

Nugget diameter
= tip diameter ± 10%
20%

Fig. 11.4   Features of a spot weld

back so that the weld is torn apart. If the weld is satisfactory, a tear goes round the edge of the nugget in the sheet which is being stripped back. A slug of metal is left on the other sheet showing that there was sufficient fused area to give an acceptable weld strength. On the other hand, if there has not been enough fusion the weld fractures along the interface in the peel test leaving a bright spot on the surfaces of the sheets.

Both the macrosection and peel test are destructive. After testing, the weld is useless. So, what can be done in practice to test the welding but at the same time leave serviceable welds? The answer lies in the automatic nature of the process. Weld times are short – less than one second in most cases. This is too quick for an operator to respond so the squeeze, weld and forge times as well as the electrode force and the current levels are controlled by the system. The parameters can thus be set and reproduced from one weld to another. There is no need to check each weld if we can be sure that the parameters do not drift from the original settings. This can be confirmed by doing a test weld on two pieces of sample sheet, say, every fifty welds.

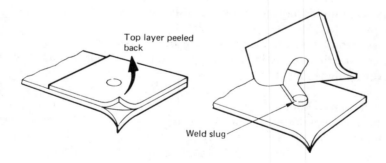

Fig. 11.5 Peel test

Resistance welding systems

So far we have concentrated on spot welding which is probably the most widely used version of resistance welding. There are two other important systems which extend the range of resistance welding applications.

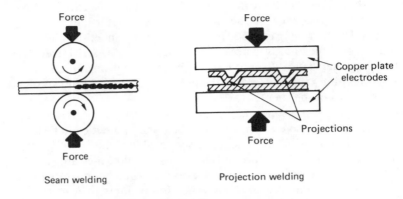

Fig. 11.6   Resistance welding systems

Seam welding

A spot welded joint is not leaktight. For this, there must be a continuous bond along the joint line – a **seam weld**.

The electrodes in seam welding are discs which are rolled along the joint line. They move continuously with pulses of current being supplied to make the weld.

Alternatively, the electrodes can be stopped while the weld is made and then rotated to the next position. This produces a series of overlapping elongated spot welds – **stitch welding**.

Projection welding

This technique differs significantly from either spot or seam welding. The current is concentrated into a small area by making projections on the surface of one of the sheets. The joint is assembled so that the projections are on the inside (i.e. at the interface) and there is a gap between the sheets. The joint is clamped between two flat electrodes using sufficient force to hold the tips of the projections on the top sheet in contact with the surface of the lower sheet. When the current is switched on, it flows through the projections which are heated, become plastic and then fuse. The pressure applied by the electrodes forces the sheets together and the fused metal at the sites of the projections solidifies to give spot welds.

One of the main advantages of projection welding is that a number of welds can be made at the same time. This means, of course, that the welding machine must have a large capacity both in terms of electrical power and hydraulic force for the electrode plattens.

Projection welding can also be used to attach studs, bolts and nuts to sheets.

Joint design

Joints for resistance spot and seam welding must always be in the form of a lap (see Fig. 1.1, page 2).

In most fabrications this requirement can be readily accommodated and is often used to strengthen the component. For example, using a flanged joint can improve the rigidity of a corner joint in a box. On the other hand, lapped joints mean an increase in weight compared with the simple butt and T-joints used for arc welding. Flanged joints also mean an extra operation in preparing the joint for welding unless the flanging can be an integral part of the forming process for the component.

Such factors are largely concerned with the economics of the operation. A more important design consideration is the need to get at both sides of the joint so that the electrodes can apply force at right angles to the sheet surfaces. Electrodes can be bent to make access easier.

A technique called **series welding** enables them to be positioned on one side of the joint provided a copper bar can be placed on the other side (Fig. 11.7).

A further consideration in designing joints for resistance welding is the spacing of the spot welds. If they are too close together, the weld size is reduced. A completed spot weld offers an easy path for the welding current. Some of the current supplied to make a new weld will be shared with the preceding, finished weld – this is called **shunting** (Fig. 11.8).

To some extent shunting can be compensated for by increasing the current for the second weld. But, if the spacing is too small, the shunting effect will be appreciable and there will be insufficient current to make a satisfactory weld. As a general rule, the pitch spacing between welds (i.e. weld centre to weld centre) should not be less than three times the diameter of the tip of the electrode. At this spacing, only about 3% of the current is shunted.

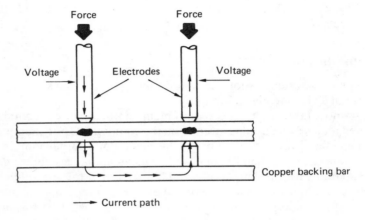

Fig. 11.7 Series welding

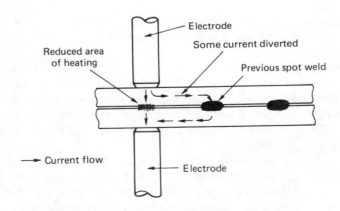

Fig. 11.8 Shunting in spot welding

Machine controls

There are three main variables to be set and controlled in resistance spot welding.

1 **Current**

On most machines the control knob for current is marked 'Heat control'. With small or low cost units this is simply a switch which alters the input to the transformer. Larger and more sophisticated machines still use a switched control but only for coarse adjustment. Fine control is achieved by solid state circuits.

Guidance for the correct heat setting is given in equipment manuals, but the optimum current is determined by trials on sample strips which are then tested by peeling.

2 **Electrode force**

Although electrode force can be measured using special pressure gauges, for general work it is more useful to judge the best setting from trial welds on steel strip. The aim should be to produce a weld with about 10% indentation at the surface. If metal is splashed from the interface when the weld is being made it could indicate that the electrode force is too low.

3 **Time**

Squeeze time and hold time are rarely critical and for most purposes can be about 20 cycles and 10 cycles respectively.

Establishing the weld time is more difficult because it is related to current. The higher the current the shorter the weld time needed and vice versa.

A starting point for the time can be calculated from the following formula:

$$\text{Weld time (in seconds)} = \frac{\text{sheet thickness (mm)}}{5}$$

$$\text{Number of cycles} = \frac{\text{Weld time (secs)} \times 100}{2}$$

As an example, take a spot weld between two pieces of 1.0 mm (20 swg) sheet.

$$\text{Weld time} = \frac{1}{5} = 0.2 \text{ seconds}$$

$$\text{Number of cycles} = \frac{0.2 \times 100}{2} = 10 \text{ cycles}$$

To establish the best conditions, the timer can be set to this value and a test weld made. If the diameter is too large, either the current or the time can be reduced and further tests made until an acceptable result is obtained. It is best to avoid very short weld times.

Reflecting on this sequence of test welds needed to determine optimum conditions, it is not difficult to see why resistance welding is not often used for making only small numbers of spot welds. A lengthy test programme is justifiable when there are thousands of components to be welded or when dealing with an expensive component.

This is not to say that resistance welding cannot be used by the small jobbing shop or the DIY worker. The benefits of fast, low distortion welding with little manual skill make resistance welding an attractive proposition on steel sheet in the range 0.8 mm to 1.2 mm (22 swg to 18 swg). A record of settings which have been found to give satisfactory results can provide sufficient data to enable spot welding conditions to be set up quickly for sheet steel in these thicknesses.

12

Welding Applications

From what has been written in the previous chapters it can be seen that welding is widely used in a variety of industries. Each application has its own requirements, and specialised knowledge, based on experience, has been accumulated in individual industries such as aerospace, automobile, nuclear power and shipbuilding.

In this chapter we will look at four specific applications of fusion welding which frequently raise questions about techniques and procedures – sheets, sections, pipes and castings.

Most of the components welded in DIY applications are made from either thin metal (sheet) or thin walled sections. The latter could be:

- round – tubes or pipes
- rectangular – RHS (rectangular hollow sections)
- angular – L, U or H in cross-section; this group includes RSJ (rolled steel joist)

The term *thin* is not very precise but it is frequently used to describe metal with a thickness of less than 6 mm. Thin walled pipes for carrying liquids or tubes used for structures typically have a wall thickness of 3 mm to 6 mm. Flat material in this thickness would be called plate whereas sheets are normally within the range 0.8 mm to 3.2 mm.

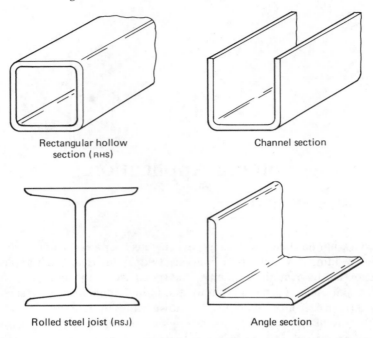

Rectangular hollow
section (RHS)

Channel section

Rolled steel joist (RSJ)

Angle section

Fig. 12.1   Typical sections used in welded fabrications

Welding sheet metal

The purchaser of sheet metal can often be confused by the different
measures used for thickness. Some thicknesses are quoted in millimetres whilst others may be fractions or decimals of an inch. Until
the recent advent of metrication the most common measure was
the Standard Wire Gauge (swg). The relationship between these
various measures is given in Table 12.

Fusion welding of sheet

There are two principal problems in the fusion welding of sheet:

- controlling penetration
- minimising distortion

Table 12
Comparison of sheet thicknesses

Metric (mm)	swg	Imperial (in)
0.7	22	–
0.9	20	$\frac{1}{32}$
1.2	18	$\frac{3}{64}$
1.6	16	$\frac{1}{16}$
2.0	14	$\frac{5}{64}$
2.5	12	$\frac{3}{32}$
3.2	10	$\frac{1}{8}$

Controlling penetration

At first sight, welding sheet metal should offer few difficulties. Because it is thin, heat is not conducted away from the joint line as fast as it would be with thick plate, so it should be easier to obtain fusion even with welding sets of limited capacity. There should also be no problems in obtaining penetration through the thickness, at least up to 3 mm thick, and there is no need to bevel the edges of the joint. A square edge can be used for butt joints.

However, in practice it is all too easy to penetrate through the joint with the result that the weld pool collapses and a hole is formed.

The prime task is to control the heat input. The amount of heat supplied is governed by the current, in arc welding, or the nozzle size, in gas welding. These are chosen to match the thickness of the sheet and are set before welding begins. Once the operation is under way, the heat input is dependent on the travel speed. By travelling faster or slower the size of the weld pool and the amount of penetration can be reduced or increased. Some control of penetration can also be achieved by adjusting the electrode or torch angle – flatter angles give reduced penetration – and arc length (in MMA and TIG welding).

Penetration control in butt joints can be assisted by using a backing bar. This is a strip of copper with a groove along the centre (Fig. 3.6 page 39). The sheets are clamped firmly to the bar with the joint aligned with the groove.

The bar performs two functions. Firstly, it conducts the heat away from the joint area – this gives more latitude in adjusting the heat input. Secondly, it supports the penetration bead in the groove but great care must be taken to avoid the copper being melted into the weld pool since this would lead to cracking in the weld metal. The risk of this is very high with aluminium and it is more common practice with this metal to use stainless steel backing bars.

Perhaps one of the most important factors is joint fit-up, i.e. the alignment of the plates, the accuracy of the root gap and the uniformity of the angle between the joint faces. If the root gap varies, it becomes difficult to maintain a uniform travel speed and overheating, followed by the formation of a hole, can quickly result. This is particularly the case in T-joints where the problem of balancing the distribution of heat between the joint components becomes much more difficult to solve if filler metal has to be used to bridge and fill an oversize gap.

In the butt joints, the gap between the sheet edges closes as the weld is progressed along the joint line. Tack welds at intervals of about 40 mm help to keep the gap open.

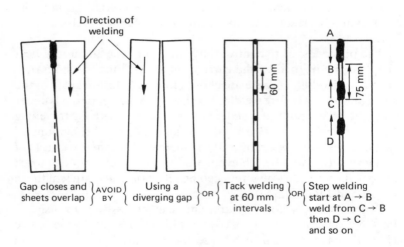

Fig. 12.2   Controlling gap size in butt welding of sheet

Minimising distortion

Distortion results from the change in dimensions of the metal caused by the heating and cooling which takes place during welding. As heating is an essential part of fusion welding, distortion cannot be eliminated. The best we can do is to adopt practices which reduce the effects of expansion and contraction in the joint to a minimum.

The first critical decision relates to the choice of welding process. Oxy-acetylene welding, because it is slow, gives a wide spread of heat and this leads to more distortion. Ideally the HAZ should be as narrow as possible and so a faster welding process should give lower levels of distortion. This is in fact the case with MIG/MAG welding which offers the lowest level of distortion of all the manual welding systems. In comparison, one of the great attractions of resistance welding is the absence of significant amounts of distortion.

The next most important factor is joint fit-up. As with the control of penetration, variations in the root gap in both butt and T-joints are critical. Apart from the fact that gap filling slows down the welding operation, giving a wider heated band, the heat input is not constant along the length of the joint. Local hot spots are formed leading to variable expansion and buckling. In a similar way, accurate alignment of the sheets is also crucial.

Clamping the joint can be useful in minimising distortion (Fig. 3.9 page 43). In this connection, the clamp performs three main functions:

- helps to ensure correct alignment
- restrains movement during heating and cooling
- restricts the spread of heat, thus reducing the width of the heated band in which expansion and contraction occur

Brazing and soldering

Although welding is often the first choice for the joining of sheet metal, brazing and soldering are widely used especially for automated or mechanised production. Brazing in particular offers an attractive alternative to welding, even for one-off jobs, where minimum distortion is a prime requirement.

In concept, brazing and soldering are identical. The joint is normally in the form of a lap. Liquid metal is introduced into a narrow gap between the mating surfaces so that it can provide a metallic bond when it has solidified. The melting point of the filler is below that of the parent metal. Fusion of the joint surfaces does not take place but the filler must be able to 'wet' and flow over them. Wetting can happen only if the surfaces are clean and free of oxides. This is achieved in both brazing and soldering by melting a flux into the joint ahead of the filler metal.

The main difference between brazing and soldering is the melting point of the filler. Brazing metals have melting points in excess of 450°C whereas those used for soldering melt at temperatures below 300°C. Silver soldering is a form of brazing using a silver alloy filler which melts between 500°C and 600°C.

In general terms, brazed joints tend to have higher strengths than the soldered equivalent. Often soldered joints are folded to give mechanical locking in addition to the soldered bond (Figs. 12.3 and 12.4). With both techniques, the gap between the sheets at the joint interface is critical. To achieve complete filling of the gap and maximum strength, the filler metal must be drawn or sucked into the joint. This can only occur with small, uniform gaps. If the gap is too large, not only is it difficult to fill, but also the strength of the joint is reduced.

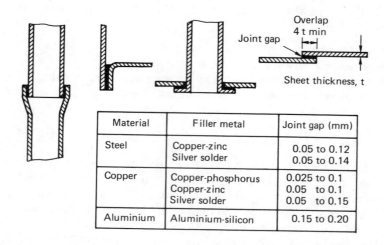

Material	Filler metal	Joint gap (mm)
Steel	Copper-zinc Silver solder	0.05 to 0.12 0.05 to 0.14
Copper	Copper-phosphorus Copper-zinc Silver solder	0.025 to 0.1 0.05 to 0.1 0.05 to 0.15
Aluminium	Aluminium-silicon	0.15 to 0.20

Fig. 12.3   Joints for brazing

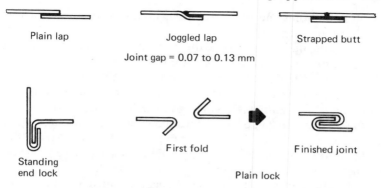

Fig. 12.4 Typical soldered joints

A variety of heating methods ranging from gas torches to ovens or furnaces is found in manufacturing practice. For manual brazing, the most common source of heat is a gas flame. As there is no need to melt the parent metal the flame temperature can be lower than that required for welding. Both oxy-acetylene and oxy-propane torches can therefore be used for brazing. Air-gas torches are suitable for soldering as the joint temperatures are much lower. The alternative is a soldering iron – particularly useful for small components.

Mild or carbon steels, stainless steels and copper can be readily brazed and soldered, but it is very difficult to join aluminium by these methods. Some success can be achieved by brazing pure aluminium with an aluminium-silicon filler and a suitable flux. The temperature of the joint must be carefully controlled to avoid the risk of overheating and melting. The flux must be completely removed after brazing, otherwise it rapidly corrodes the aluminium in damp service conditions. In the jobbing shop and for DIY work it is usually better to use epoxy-resin bonding if welding is unacceptable or not possible for aluminium.

A typical welding or brazing sequence would be:

1 Thoroughly clean the surfaces of the joint.
2 Coat the mating surfaces of the joint with flux.
3 Assemble the joint making sure that the gap is the correct size and uniform.

4 Heat the joint and the surrounding area to a distance of about 25 mm on each side.

5 When the flux has melted, withdraw the flame and touch the tip of the filler rod onto the edge of the joint. If the filler melts and flows into the joint, the temperature is correct. If the filler does not melt, move the rod away from the surface of the sheet. Heat the joint area until it is hot enough to melt the filler. Do not melt the filler in the flame – metal will flow into the joint only when the surfaces are at the right temperature. If they are cold, the filler forms globules or balls of metal which just rest on the surface and do not bond to the parent material.

6 When the correct temperature has been attained, draw the filler along the joint. Adjust the speed to allow the joint to fill. Occasionally heat the joint with the flame to keep the filling action going.

7 Allow the filler to solidify, then plunge the joint into cold water to break up and remove the flux.

Pipe welding

The terms *pipe* and *tube* are often confused. For the purposes of our present discussion we can consider that a pipe carries either a liquid or a gas while a tube is used for the construction of frames and structural work. Both are round, of course, and ideally we should have full penetration in butt welds in both pipes and tubes. In practice, however, this may not be so important in tubing used in lightly loaded structures. On the other hand, where a pipe is carrying a liquid, especially if it is of a corrosive nature, not only is full penetration needed but the profile of the penetration bead can be important. For example, some Codes and Standards require that the penetration bead should be uniform round the bore of the pipe and should not exceed 3 mm in height.

Welding procedures for pipes and tubes are essentially similar to those used for sheet and plate. The particular skill which makes this type of application difficult is accommodating the changes in position of the weld pool.

The easiest way to weld pipe is to turn it while the weld is being deposited. If the speed of rotation matches the travel speed for welding, the electrode can be kept in the same position. This

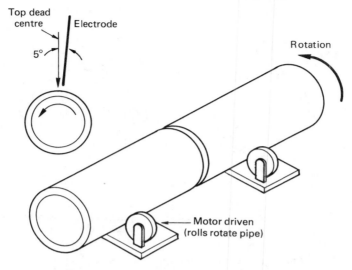

Fig. 12.5 Rotating a pipe during welding

effectively eliminates any need to adjust electrode angle and position to allow for the curvature of the pipe. Also, if the arc is kept at the top of the pipe it is easier to control the flow of the molten weld metal.

If the pipe cannot be rotated, the position of welding changes as the weld progresses around the joint (Fig. 12.6). Starting at the bottom, the first part of the weld is deposited in the overhead position. This merges into the vertical and then to the flat position at the top of the pipe.

Mostly, this is the technique used for all butt welds in pipe, although the first or root run with MAG welding of steel pipe can be made with a vertical-down technique, i.e. starting at the top and working down to the underside of the pipe; filling runs on thicker walled pipe would then be deposited starting at the bottom. The main exception to this is **stovepipe welding** which is employed on large diameter pipe used for gas and oil transmission lines. In this technique, a cellulose electrode (BS639:E4311C or AWS:E6010) is used and the welds are deposited vertically down. In addition there are constraints on the time lapse between runs to avoid the joint cooling down too much.

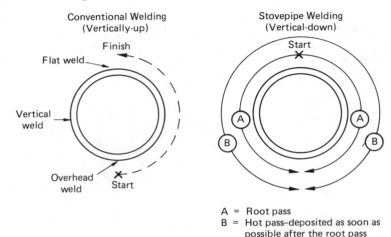

A = Root pass
B = Hot pass–deposited as soon as
possible after the root pass

Fig. 12.6 Welding pipe which is fixed in position

Pipe welding introduces an additional factor into the choice of process – ease of manipulation. This is influenced by the amount of access to the joint. Often pipes are located close to a wall or to the floor. In situations of restricted access, oxy-acetylene welding often offers a better chance of success than MIG/MAG or MMA welding. OA welding is also more attractive with pipes less than 50 mm diameter where the rapid changes of curvature make manipulation of a MIG/MAG gun or an MMA electrode difficult. With larger diameters, however, the slow speeds of OA give rise to local distortion.

There are three types of joint used in pipe welding: flange, butt and branch (Fig. 12.7). In all three, fit-up is a crucial factor. As purchased, pipes are not exactly round. There may be small variations in diameter and more often than not there is a slight ovality. As a result there is a risk of misalignment and pipes should be rotated to get the best match between mating ends before tack welding or clamping.

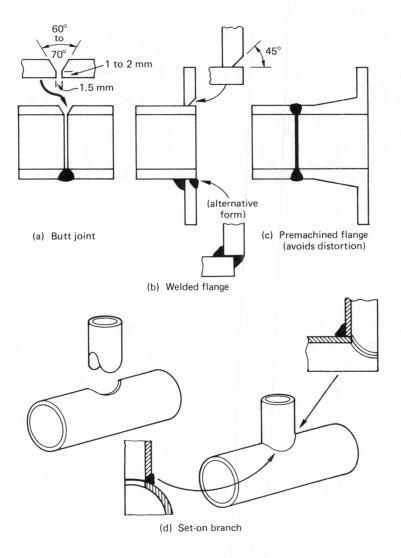

Fig. 12.7 Typical pipe and tube joints

Welding sections

In the main, sections offer few specific problems in welding. They call for short lengths of welding and particular attention must be paid to the starts and stops which can make up an appreciable portion of the completed weld. The main consideration is the achievement of penetration at the corners of sections made from thicker material. With this in mind it is often worthwhile bevelling the edges even though the thickness may be only of the order of 3 mm. Pre-formed backing strips are available for RHS which help to ease the problem of controlling penetration. Unlike the backing bars used when welding sheets, the root run in a backed RHS joint penetrates into the backing strip which thus becomes part of the finished weld.

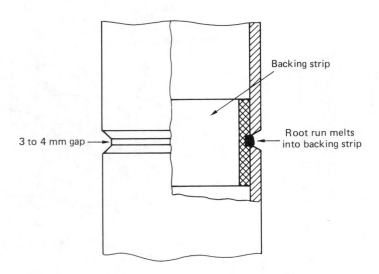

Fig. 12.8   Using a backing strip with RHS and tubes

Repairing castings

One of the tasks a welder may need to tackle is the repair of castings.

With many components, especially those of complex shape, it is preferable to use castings rather than machine them from the solid or fabricate them from a number of pieces using welding, brazing or soldering. In the casting process, molten metal is poured into a cavity which has the shape of the finished component. The mould can be made from sand or some other disposable material, or it can be machined from a block of metal and used time and again.

In general, castings have less ductility than, say, plates or pipes. Some castings are very brittle and readily crack if they are bent. Cast iron pipes fracture if struck by a hammer. Flanges in zinc diecastings, such as the carburettor in a car engine, crack if the securing bolts are overtightened. At first sight, welding offers a ready method of repairing such fractures. However, many metals used for castings do not have good weldability and it is important to assess this aspect carefully before a repair is attempted.

Both cast iron and cast steel are suitable for fusion welding. Some aluminium alloy castings can be welded by the TIG process, but it requires a high degree of skill to achieve satisfactory results as the weld pool tends to be very fluid and difficult to control. Many aluminium casting alloys are not suitable, however, because the weld metal is prone to cracking. Perhaps the most common need for repair is to zinc alloy diecastings, but these are not suitable for welding and alternative jointing methods such as adhesive bonding must be used.

Repairing cast iron

Success in using welding to repair fractured cast iron components is hampered by two problems. Firstly, the cooling rates experienced when using both arc and oxy-acetylene welding can cause excessive hardening in the HAZ. This in turn gives a high risk of cracking after welding. Secondly, the contraction of the weld metal coupled with the highly localised heating created by welding can set up stress in other parts of the component. Because cast iron has low ductility, this stress can produce further cracking, remote from the welding which is being used to repair the first fracture.

Fortunately, both of these problems can be offset by preheating the component and maintaining it at temperature until after the welding operation has been completed. In Chapter 5 preheating of steel was proposed as a method of controlling cracks in the HAZ of higher strength steels. For those materials, we were talking of raising the temperature of the joint area to somewhere between 100° and 175°C. In the case of cast iron the preheat temperature is between 600° and 700°C and often the whole of the component must be heated to avoid the build-up of local stress concentrations.

The extent of the preheat is governed by the location of the repair and the mass or size of the component. There are three possibilities:

1 If at least one of the pieces making up the joint is free to move, the contraction of the weld can be easily accommodated and a local preheat is sufficient to reduce the risk of hardening in the HAZ.

2 When the fracture has taken place in a rigid member of the component, e.g. the rim of a wheel or a strut in a machine frame (Fig. 12.9), preheat is again needed in the area of the fracture. But overall preheat can be avoided by heating just selected parts of the component.

3 Where the repair is to be done in an area surrounded by a large mass of metal, overall preheating is essential. An example is a crack emanating from a hole in a large pump body or a cylinder block.

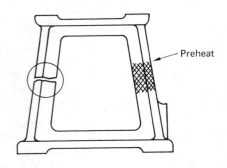

Fig. 12.9 Typical frame fracture

Both oxy-acetylene and MMA welding can be used for cast iron. The best results are obtained using small weld runs – **stringer beads**. These are more easily deposited by MMA and in general the preference is for this process using nickel or nickel-iron electrodes.

A typical welding sequence for welding cast iron would be:

1 Grind out the crack to leave a V-preparation with a 90° included angle (Fig. 12.10).
2 Thoroughly degrease.
3 Preheat in an oven or surround the component with fire bricks and use a propane torch. Check the temperature with a thermocouple or other measuring device.
4 Use small diameter electrodes and deposit stringer beads. Place one bead on each side of the groove and then deposit another between them. After each weld run has been deposited, remove the flux and lightly hammer (peen) the weld metal before depositing the next run.
5 When the weld is complete, cool slowly in the oven or cover the component with insulating material.

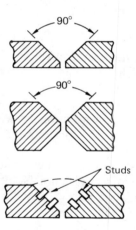

Fig. 12.10   Preparing cast-iron joint edges for fusion welding

Glossary of Terms

These definitions are taken from BS499: Welding terms and symbols.

angle of bevel (angle of preparation)   The angle at which the edge of a component is prepared for making a weld.

arc eye   Irritation of the eye caused by exposure to radiation from an electric arc.

backfire   Retrogression of the flame into the blowpipe neck or body with rapid self-extinction.

base metal   See *parent metal*.

bead   A single run of weld metal on a surface.

blowpipe (torch)   A device for mixing and burning gases to produce a flame for welding, brazing, braze welding, cutting, heating and similar operations.

burn-off rate   (1) In friction welding. The rate of shortening of the components during application of the friction force. (2) In arc welding. The linear rate of consumption of a consumable electrode.

CO_2 welding   Metal-arc welding in which a bare wire electrode is used, the arc and molten pool being shielded with carbon dioxide.

crater pipe   A depression due to shrinkage at the end of a run where the source of heat was removed.

cycle   An arbitrary unit of time, of duration equal to that of one cycle of the alternating current supply. Normally in Great Britain this is 1/50 s.

deposited metal   Filler metal after it becomes part of a weld or joint.

dilution   The alteration of composition of the metal deposited from a filler wire or electrode due to mixing with the melted parent material. It is usually expressed as the percentage of melted parent metal in the weld metal.

duty cycle The percentage ratio of duration of current flow during a period, to the period.

edge preparation The surface prepared on the edge of a component to be welded.

electrode (arc welding electrode) A rod, tube or wire of metal or a rod of carbon between one end of which and either the work or another electrode the arc is formed. See also *resistance welding electrode*.

feather edge The edge formed at the root due to bevelling being carried through from one surface to the other.

filler metal Metal added during welding, braze welding, brazing or surfacing.

flashback Retrogression of the flame beyond the blowpipe body into the hose, with possible subsequent explosion.

flux Material used during welding, brazing or braze welding to clean the surfaces of the joint chemically, to prevent atmospheric oxidation and to reduce impurities. In arc welding, many other substances, which perform special functions, are added.

fusion penetration In fusion welding, the depth to which the parent metal has been fused.

gas welding Fusion welding, with or without filler metal, in which the heat for welding is produced by the combustion of a fuel gas or gases with an admixture of oxygen.

hard facing (hard surfacing) The application of a hard, wear-resistant material to the surface of a component by welding, braze welding or spraying.

heat affected zone (HAZ) The part of the parent metal that is metallurgically affected by the heat of welding or thermal cutting, but not melted.

included angle (angle of preparation) The angle between the planes of the fusion faces of parts to be welded.

interface The contact area when the welding force is applied.

interpass temperature In a multi-run weld, the temperature of the weld and adjacent parent metal immediately prior to the application of the next run.

joint preparation (weld preparation) A preparation for making a connection where the individual components, suitably prepared and assembled, are joined by welding or brazing.

manual metal arc welding (MMA welding)   Metal arc welding with straight covered electrodes of a suitable length and applied by the operator without automatic or semi-automatic means of replacement. No protection in the form of a gas or mixture of gases from a separate source is applied to the arc or molten pool during welding.

metal active gas welding (MAG welding)   Gas-shielded metal arc welding using a consumable wire electrode where the shielding is provided by a shroud of active or non-inert gas or mixture of gases.

metal inert gas welding (MIG welding)   Gas-shielded metal arc welding using a consumable wire electrode where the shielding is provided by a shroud of inert gas.

melt run   A line of parent metal that has been melted by passing a welding flame or arc along the surface of the metal.

molten pool (weld pool)   The pool of liquid metal formed during fusion welding. In electroslag welding the term includes the slag bath.

parent metal (base metal)   Metal to be joined or surfaced by welding, braze welding or brazing.

penetration bead   Weld metal protruding through the root of a fusion weld made from one side only.

preheating temperature   The temperature immediately prior to the commencement of welding resulting from the heating of the parent metal in the region of the weld.

pressure regulator (gas regulator)   A device for attachment to a gas cylinder or pipeline for reducing and regulating the gas pressure to the working pressure required.

rate of travel (travel speed)   The time required to complete a unit length of a single run of weld or melt run.

resistance welding   Welding in which, at some stage in the process, force is applied to surfaces in contact and in which the heat for welding is produced by the passage of electric current through the electrical resistance at, and adjacent to, these surfaces.

resistance welding electrode (electrode)   A replaceable portion of a resistance welding machine which transmits current, and usually applies force to the workpiece.

run (pass)   The metal melted or deposited during one passage of an electrode, torch or blowpipe.

root run (root pass)   The first run deposited in the root of a multi-run weld.

sealing run (backing run)   The final run deposited on the root side of a fusion weld.

seam welding   Resistance welding in which force is applied continuously and current intermittently to produce a linear weld, the workpiece being between two electrode wheels or between an electrode wheel and an electrode bar. The wheels apply the force and current and rotate continuously during the making of the linear weld.

spot welding   Resistance welding in which a weld is produced at a spot in the workpiece between electrodes, the weld being of approximately the same area as the electrode tips, or as the smaller of tips of differing size. Force is applied to the spot, usually through the electrodes, continuously throughout the process.

stitch welding   Spot welding in which successive welds overlap.

stringer bead   A run of weld metal with little or no weaving motion.

submerged arc welding (SA welding)   Metal arc welding in which a bare wire electrode or strip is used, the arc(s) being enveloped in a granular flux, some of which fuses to form a removable covering of slag on the weld.

toe   The boundary between a weld face and the parent metal or between runs.

travel speed   See *rate of travel.*

tungsten inert gas welding (TIG welding)   Gas-shielded arc welding using a non-consumable pure or activated tungsten electrode where the shielding is provided by a shroud of inert gas.

weaving   Transverse oscillation of an electrode or of a blowpipe nozzle during the deposition of weld metal.

weld edge   See *toe.*

weld face   The surface of a fusion weld exposed on the side from which the weld has been made.

weld metal   All metal melted during the making of a weld and retained in the weld.

weld nugget   A zone in a resistance weld where the metal has been melted.

weld pool   See *molten pool*.

weld preparation   See *joint preparation*.

welding   An operation in which two or more parts are united, by means of heat or pressure or both, in such a way that there is continuity in the nature of the metal between these parts. A filler metal, the melting temperature of which is of the same order as that of the parent metal, may or may not be used.

welding speed   The length of single or multi-run weld completed in a unit of time.

These definitions are reproduced by permission of the British Standards Institution, from whom copies of the standard may be purchased (see p. 186).

Appendix
Useful Information

1   Further reading

For a broader view of fabrication:
Welding and fabrication technology
W. Kenyon
Pitman, 1982

For more detail of craft aspects:
Welding craft practice, volumes 1 and 2 (2nd Edition)
N. Parkin and C. R. Flood
Pergamon, 1979

General welding and cutting Module F10 Instruction Manual
EITB
54 Clarendon Road, Watford
WD1 1LB

For a more extensive treatment of welding technology:
Principles of welding technology (2nd Edition)
L. Gourd
Edward Arnold, 1986

**For an advanced study of
welding processes:**
Welding processes
P. T. Houldcroft
Cambridge University Press,
1977

**For more knowledge about
non-destructive testing of welds:**
Introduction to NDT of welds
R. Halmshaw
The Welding Institute, 1987

**For an introduction to design
aspects:**
Welded joint design
J. G. Hicks
Granada Publishing, 1979

2   Videos and films

The Welding Institute publish a number of videos and films related
to welding. In particular, there is a series of videos aimed at the DIY
user of welding and those who work in garages or similar establish-
ments. The videos cover the practical techniques of MIG/MAG,
MMA and OA welding.

Details from: The Welding Institute
                Abington Hall,
                Abington,
                Cambridge CB1 6AL

3   Practical training

Training in the practical skills of welding is available from three
sources:

Colleges of Further Education – addresses are usually in the local
telephone directory but information can be obtained from The
Education Officer at the appropriate County Offices.

Skillcentres which are operated by the Skills Training Agency – information about these is available at the local Job Centre.

Commercial Schools – usually these offer short full-time courses designed to suit the needs of local industry; it is not always easy to obtain details of these schools but distributors of welding equipment can often give advice.

4 Qualifications

Qualifications in welding fall into three groups:

Approval tests (see page 115) which are job related and are normally arranged by an employer.

Information about the HVCA scheme can be obtained from:
Heating and Ventilating Contractors Association
ESCA House
34 Palace Court
Bayswater
London W2 4JG

Educational awards in welding technology based on attendance at courses.

Craft education certificates are issued by:
City and Guilds Institute
46 Britannia Street
London WC1X 9RG

Craft practice certificates (up to BS4872 level) are issued by:
EMFEC
Robins Wood House
Robins Wood Road
Aspley
Nottingham NG8 3NH

National and Higher National Certificates are under the control of:
Business and Technician Education Council
Central House
Upper Woburn Place
London WC1H 0HH

Postgraduate courses are run by:

- Brunel University
- Cranfield Institute of Technology
- Constantine Polytechnic, Middlesbrough
- Paisley College of Technology
- The Welding Institute

Specialist Certificates are issued by The Welding Institute

Chartered and Registered status – details from The Professional Registrar at The Welding Institute.

5   Equipment supplies

Addresses of distributors of welding equipment and consumables can be obtained from:

The Association of Welding Distributors
1 Hull Road
York YO1 3SF

6   British standards

British Standards provide a valuable source of information on welding and give a guide to good practice. A price list for Standards related to welding can be obtained from:

BSI Sale Department
Linford Wood
Milton Keynes MK14 6LE

They can also be borrowed from local public libraries.

There is a large number of standards which concern welding in one way or another. The following is a short selection of those which specifically relate to the subjects discussed in this book; in some cases the titles have been abbreviated.

General

BS499 Pt 1: 1983	Glossary of terms
BS499 Pt 2: 1980	Symbols for welding

Practices

BS1140: 1980	Resistance welding of steel sheet
BS1724: 1959	Bronze welding

BS1821: 1982	Oxy-acetylene welding of steel pipes
BS2633: 1987	Arc welding steel pipes
BS3019 Pt 1: 1984	TIG welding aluminium, magnesium and their alloys
BS3019 Pt 2: 1960	TIG welding austenitic stainless steel
BS3571 Pt 1: 1985	MIG welding of aluminium and its alloys
BS5135: 1984	Arc welding carbon manganese steels

Consumables

BS639: 1986	Covered carbon manganese steel electrodes for MMA welding
BS1453: 1972 (1987)	Filler materials for gas welding
BS2901 Parts 1 to 5	Filler rods and wire for gas shielded welding
BS4165: 1984	Electrode wires and fluxes for submerged arc welding of carbon manganese steels

Materials

BS970 Pt 1: 1983	Requirements for carbon, carbon manganese, alloy and stainless steels
BS1470: 1987	Specification for wrought aluminium and aluminium alloys
BS4360: 1986	Specification for weldable structural steels

Testing

BS709: 1983	Destructive testing of fusion welded joints
BS1295: 1987	Code of practice for training in arc welding skills
BS4870 Parts 1 to 3	Approval testing of welding procedures
BS4871 Parts 1 to 3	Approval testing of welders working to approved procedures
BS4872 Parts 1 & 2	Approval testing of welders when no procedure approval is required
BS5289: 1976 (1983)	Visual inspection of fusion welded joints

Filler wires for aluminium and aluminium alloys

These may still be marked with the old BS2901 designation.

1080A	was	GIA	— pure aluminium
1050B	was	GIB	— pure aluminium
5056A	was	NG6	— aluminium-magnesium
4047	was	NG2	— aluminium-10% silicon
4043	was	NG21	— aluminium-5% silicon

Index